D1134939

A MOUSE IS BORN

BY ANITA LOOS

A Mouse Is Born · Happy Birthday

Gentlemen Prefer Blondes

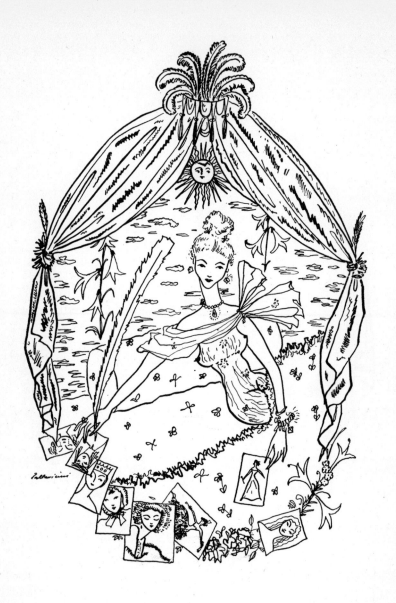

A Mouse Is Born

BY ANITA LOOS

DRAWINGS BY PALLAVICINI

Doubleday & Company, Inc., 1951
Garden City, N.Y.

*The characters and incidents in this book
are entirely the product of the author's imagination
and have no relation to any person or event in real life.*

To J.E.

19   *Everyone in Hollywood felt that your Mommy had all the requirements to star in* The Road to Coney Island.

35   *Mommy's first serious roll had several diferent dimensions, caused by portraying a cripple who was born with Sex Apeal.*

41   *Your Mommy's conception of "The Woman in Black" brought Sex into the lives of hum-drum people all over the civilized globe.*

7

53   *The part of "Crystal Carruthers" in* Adrift on the Rio *was cute, but she didn't augmint Mommy's stature as an actress, much.*

75   *In* Orient Express *my conception of Fritzi Gabour, a well-known spy, got me mentioned for the Oscar once.*

83   *Your Mommy's first starring vehickle,* The Nude Deal *was produced before Mommy was well-known, or even blonde.*

116 *This poster was drawn by some artist who never even had an interoduction to Mommy, and which I never, by no means, would ever of posed for.*

127 *In Hollywood there is an old addige that every Star has had her bubble bath.*

139 *In your Mommy's conception of Mary-the-Queen-of-the-Scotts, the Director shot eight reels of Mommy feeling sorry for myself.*

153 *The Studio decided to cheer the Publick up, so it had my authoress pen* Bettina of the Big Top.

8

163 *The Studio finally dwelved into Histry for Mommy and came up with George Sand, the well-known Tomboy.*

172 *Mommy's Producers finally took me back to the days of lighter-weight dress fabricks.*

193 *In the Three-Million-Dollar Production called La Pompadore, your Mommy portrayed a world-famous French Madam.*

207 *Came the dawn.*

9

A MOUSE IS BORN

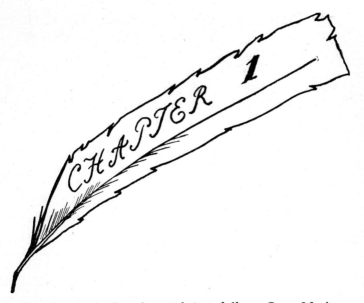

CHAPTER 1

When anybody, who's Life is as full as a Great Motion Picture Star, finds out she has to go into retiremint for months because the Greatest Thing in Life has happened to you, you really begin to worry about wasting so much time. Of course, everybody knows that the greatest thing about Motherhood is the "Sacrifices," but it is quite a shock to find out that they begin so far ahead of time.

Because the first one came when I was called upon to sacrifice the roll of Mildred in *The Road to Coney Island* because my physical adviser, Dockie Davis, discovered I was expecting our "Little Mouse." (Clyde and I love to call it our "Little Mouse" because I feel the word "mouse" is by-sexual and will fit it no matter what it turns out to be.) But Clyde was a great comfort to me in the hour of trial, because he told me to always remember that, in time, the Publick might forget *The Road to Coney Island* but our "Little Mouse" would be a comfort to us forever.

So the next great Sacrifice came when Dockie Davis told me I would have to lay in bed for the whole duration of it, because my physical condition is exceptional due to the strains I went through before making up my mind that Motherhood was even a greater career than being a Great Motion Picture Star.

And the way I came to the momentis decision of "A Career Versis Motherhood" is peculiar. Because when my Career started and I began to receive Fan Mail, my letters were so absorbant I would never of thought the day would come when I could get enough of them. But it finally turned out that there is a "catch" to those Fan Letters, because they inveritably say the same identical thing, in the same identical landguage which consists of saying "I saw you in your last picture and you was wonderful." And quite a few of those letters are even written on paper that some Fan tore off the paper some grocer wrapped the groceries up in, so they are not even very apetizing. So after a Star has received five or six million of those Fan letters, you begin to realize you must be wonderful without having to read all those monitinous letters.

But to have a "Little Mouse" can never be monitinous because you can dress it diferent every day—especially with the hundreds of Kiddie Shops that have sprouted up all over Hollywood since Babies have become the order of the day in Films by adoption or by birth.

Of course, Clyde and I could of adopted our "Little Mouse" and I could still of starred in *The Road to Coney Island*, but I felt that not having it personally was the wrong approach to Motherhood. Because Clyde is one of the most photogenique persons in the whole world, so why shouldn't we take advantage of such a great oppertunity and allow it to inherit Clyde's own personal appearance?

So, when I first went to bed to wait for our "Little Mouse," I ordered special night robes specially designed by the famous Hollywood Lingeray designer, Juel Park, who is closer to the vital things of Life in Hollywood than anybody else. And, as I am sufficiently artistic to design everything myself, I told Juel to embroider them all over with small forget-me-knots and words from the lyrics of "Sweet Mystry of Life" (At last I've found you . . . Ah . . . At last I know the meaning of it all). Because, at the beginning, I felt very emotional about the Mystry of it all. But after a few weeks of laying in bed, with Clyde away all day at the Studio, even a person that loves mysteries can get fed up with a Mystry you have to take, day in, and day out, laying down. So, I finally decided to at least improve my time, so I sent for Michele, my hair-dresser, to come to the house every day and bring one of the Studio Photographers with him and have photographs taken for the Mouse, of all my coiffeurs.

And when it came to picking out a photographer who would know how to light me in bed, the one that knew the best happened to be Lester Cummings who I was married to once.

But just as Lester was beginning to accomplish great

things, I found out that Clyde was having the House watched by deteckatives all day while he was out at Universal shooting his picture. Because Clyde has never been able to understand how Lester and I have turned out to meerly be the best of friends. And Clyde has always been so suspicious of my and Lester's friendship that, even though I have frequently been married to other husbands, it is always Lester who Clyde presumes to be jealous of. But to me, Friendship is sacred and, where Lester is concerned, I have the feeling that a Cameraman that knows how to light you in bed has just simply got to be cherished.

Well, there was really no reason for Clyde to worry about Lester and I, because everything that was going on in my boudoire was of a type to bore those deteckatives to tears. So, with nothing to interest them indoors, those deteckatives started to spend their time out in our summer house, drinking up all our liquor and consequently getting the maids into trouble. So, for the sake of harminy, I finally had to discontinue Lester.

But then I anyhow got a better idear, which is to phone to all the Studios I ever worked at, and get them to send over the Stills of my various characterizations, so the Mouse can have them to look at, in an album, through the years.

But sometimes the Golden California Sunshine pouring on my taffeta bed-spred became so monitinous, I began to think how delightful it would be if Clyde and I could take a trip East, where I could at least look out the window and watch the seasons change. So one night I mentioned it to Clyde and, to my astroundmint, he asked why I didn't go ahead and take the trip alone, and

16

he would join me after his picture got Pre-Viewed in several months.

So I begun to worry, to think that Clyde could think of being seperated at the most Sacred Period of our lives. And besides, this was the ideal time for us to get acquainted, because our wedding took place so unexpectedly that Clyde loves to tell how he didn't even know, at the time, the color hair his little wife was born with.

And then, laying in bed alone, day after day, I began to be haunted by the specter of the new Swedish Film Star that Universal imported from Sweeden to play opasite Clyde. For Clyde is the only Real Thing I have got in my Life. And I began to ask myself, "What if Inga Swansen has taken it into her head that Clyde is the only real thing in *her* Life?" Because we Film Stars all live in a world of Make Believe, after all.

So I would toss, and turn, and grit my fingernails and wait for Clyde to come Home every afternoon from Universal City and declare that he cared for me, yet. But every day he got Home later and later. And even when he got here, all he wanted to do was toss himself on the bed-spred and pour his troubles out. But it only made me begin to suspect that Clyde was looking for some kind of an alibi to keep him off the subjeck of our Great Love for one another.

But every moment that Clyde ever spends in shooting a picture is crucial. And, in the picture he was shooting then, Clyde's alibi was that he was having even a more crucial time than usual. In the first place, his Director didn't know anything about Shakespeare, because he came from a stage theatre in London called the

Old Vick, where Clyde said it was evidint that they had never heard tell of a Profile. And that Director kept letting the wrong side of Clyde's Profile get picked up by the Camera. And Clyde said, "As if it isn't enough of a task to make 'Richard the Third' attractive to my Fans, even with my best Profile!" Because Clyde felt, from the beginning, that the roll didn't have any oppertunities. And Clyde is not dificult to please, because all he ever asks of any roll is that he can be adoreable.

But what made things even more trying was that, night after night, Clyde's sleeping pills refused to work. So to keep me from finding out he couldn't go to Sleep because he was thinking of Inga Swansen, he would pretend he was worrying about his Profiles. And then he would deviate between his dressing room (where he would look at all his Profiles in the three-way mirror) and the Rumpus Room (where he would run Close-Ups of them on our projection machine). And all I could do was to lay there and wait for my own sleeping pills to work, and pray for Clyde to not let our Honeymoon come to an end, just when Motherhood is beginning to deepen our experience.

Well, when Clyde finally did come to bed, I would be able to doze off by clutching him, but at 6 A.M. he would make so much noise getting out of bed, so he could get out to Universal City, so he could put on a special make-up that encluded both a limp and a hump,

 Everyone in Hollywood felt that your Mommy had all the requiremints to star in The Road to Coney Island.

that he would always wake me up. And then, every morning when Clyde walked out of the house, it seemed to be symbolick that he wasn't ever going to come back Home again. So then I would start tossing and turning again for the duration of the day.

Well, yesterday morning about eleven o'clock, my Business Manager came to the house to pay me his respecks. But the relationship between Morrie and I has been on tender hooks from the momint he had his first inkling about our "Little Mouse." Because, where any of we Film Stars are concerned, Morrie has no toleration for Kiddies. And he loves to say that the most harrowing part of being a Business Manager is the business of having to constantly keep check on we Stars as regards the prospects of having one. And Morrie loves to say that no sooner did he used to find out that *I* was in the clear than it was time to begin worrying about Gloria Trent out at the Medalion Studio. And if Gloria was Okay, he couldn't even take time to sigh with relief, before he had to jump in his car and go check on Enid Holbrook at Republic. And after Enid came Bunny Ambrose at 20th Century, and Sylvia West at Warners. And by that time, it was time to begin worrying about *me* again, in the same old vicious circle that drives a Business Manager out of his mind in Hollywood. And Morrie loves to say it is indignant for a bachelor, like him, to put in his time keeping check on so many of we girls. And sometimes he wishes he could be thrown up on a desert island where, as far as the eye can reach, there wouldn't be a single Calendar.

And Morrie loves to complain that whenever we Film Stars meet some Wolf who either has eyelashes or a pair of shoulders, we never have any forethought or pause to consider the risk to the Stock Holders. But I just used to laugh at Morrie and tell him not to try and hold his breath until the Publick begins to clammer for the kind of Film Stars that have forethought.

So when the time finally came that I had to let Morrie know I was guilty of our "Little Mouse," no amount of sleeping pills seemed to do me any good. Because Morrie had never even given his consent to me marrying Clyde in the first place, so I knew how discouradged he would be to hear there was going to be a tie between Clyde and I that binds.

And sometimes I have an inkling that, in addition to Morrie's efficiency as my Business Manager, his feelings for me may be even a little bit personal. Because Morrie never regulates any of my business affairs to his staff, but always attends to them himself. For instants, if I suddenly need a new panty-girdle to wear at the Pree-meer of some new picture, it is never Morrie's secretary, Hazel, who runs over to Magnin's to buy it, but Morrie who drops everything and goes out to buy it himself. And every time I can't recall where I parked my car, it is always Morrie who jumps into his own roadster and makes a tour of Hollywood, Beverly Hills, Westwood and even Los Angeles to find it. And one time when I cried because Dockie Davis proscribed me to take a table-spoon of Castor Oil, Morrie swallowed one him-self, just to show me how it could be done. So I think such efficiency is almost beyond the business of even a Film Star's Business Manager.

Well, when I had to tell Morrie about our "Little Mouse" I decided against holding a confidential luncheon at Romanoff's, as the custom is with Business Managers. Because everything that's said there, in confidants, becomes the public property of all the Gossip Collomists and all the other Film Stars eating luncheon with their Business Managers, and the whole mob of Tourists to the Southland that sit there watching every mouthful we put in. So I decided to go to Morrie's Office where his screams would be a strictly private matter betwixt the two of us.

But that day I walked into Morrie's inner office I was even more nervous than the day I received a summons to the Office of Mr. Louis B. Mayer, himself, and had to cross all that expense of carpet which ultimately leads to his Desk.

So I thought the least vialent way to let the blow fall was to tell Morrie I had decided that the roll of Mildred in *The Road to Coney Island* didn't have deminsions enough to add anything to my Stature in Films. But the momint I told him that I intended to turn Mildred down, he guessed the reason why and his looks, which are inveritably dark, began to concentrate until they actually became black. And he grabbed that tell-tail Calendar off his desk and started to tear it in a hundred pieces.

And from that moment on, Morrie's voice could be heard all the way from Beverly Hills to Burbank, asking why, of all the husbands I had picked up, I had had to pick on Clyde Babcock to perpetrate for posterity.

But I am not going to go into all the unpleasant details now, because there's no sense in exposing our "Little Mouse" to such landguage more than once and, instead of being a "Little Mouse," have it born screaming like a McKaw.

So from that day on, Morrie and I hardly have to say anything to each other but "Hello" in order to start a quarrel. But the morning he came to the house to pay his respects, I was feeling so depressed that even a quarrel would of seemed welcome. And I would of loved to un-pent my emotions and told Morrie my suspicions about Clyde and Inga, except that he is able to say "I told you so" in such an infinite number of unpleasant varieties.

So after I told Morrie about the Mouse, I had to let him set at my bedside and make left-handed remarks about what would happen to my Box Office while I was off the screen for nine months. So I couldn't help reminding Morrie what happened to my Box Office in the last deal *he* fixed up for me, where he put me and a Psychological Novel and a Director friend of his (who drinks) and two Writer friends of his (who ditto) all together in a package and sold it to Republic for Five Hundred Thousand Dollars. Because what happened was that the Director and one of the Writers couldn't understand what the Novel was all about, and the one Writer who could had to be sent to a sanitarium.

Well, whenever I want to go into the memories of that deal of Morrie's, I can always shut him up. But anytime you shut Morrie up, he walks out and leaves you alone. So that's what he did to me that morning.

And a Famous Film Star who is left alone is more alone than any other person has ever been in the whole Histry of the World, because of the contrast to our normal enviromint. And sometimes I get to thinking that if I could of stood it to be alone, I would never of gotten into this predicamint.

23

But whenever things become very, very dark, I try to concentrate on the religion of a Friend of mine who is a Gag Man at the Studio, called Skip Norton. For Skip is "In Unity," so I tried to concentrate on the Great Divine Order and ask if It would please show me some way, or other, to make the best of things.

Chapter 2

So the next morning Clyde's and my secretary, Madge, came in to get my Autograph on some checks. And when Madge started to complane that I've got to stop spending money, as usual, that belongs to Uncle Sam, as usual, I started to change the subjeck, as usual. By this time I had something defanate to talk about. Because laying here thinking of Inga Swansen being in contact all day long with Clyde had almost become an obsession.

And I couldn't help but think what an advantage she has in being Sweedish, for Sweedes are blonde by birth. And Inga was also born with the kind of eyelashes that the remainder of we Stars have to buy at Max Factors and stick on with spirit gum. But the worst thing about Inga is that her English is not fluint, and when a Star can't talk a lot, it gives Clyde all the more oppertunity to talk about himself.

So I asked Madge if she had heard whether Inga Swansen was as glamerous as all the roomers say. And Madge said the consensus is that Inga has only got to raise her eyelashes at a person, irregardless of their Sex, to create a disturbance.

Well, Madge was so upsetting that I finally told her about the deteckatives in our summer house and asked her advice as to whether Clyde had hired them as a compliment to my Sex Apeal, or whether he was meerly trying to find some kind of a retaliation against me, to cheer him up about something he shouldn't be doing himself.

So Madge said that Clyde could very easily be doing something he shouldn't, but at the same time, he couldn't of hired those deteckatives, because she would of had to write out their pay checks. So then Madge asked if there was anybody else who might be interested in getting me into trouble. But I couldn't think who it might be, so I began to get even more restless, and finally Madge said,

"I wish you'd stop turning around before you give birth to a Tibetan prayer wheel."

So I asked Madge what she meant, and I was very interested in her remarks, because they had nothing to do with anything I had ever heard before. Because to hear Madge tell of reading a book about people called Tibetans, who say their prayers with the aid of a pin-wheel and put butter in their tea, was very peculiar. And I know it must be true, because Madge is the soul of integrity. And, anyhow, I have grown to believe almost everything since the time I had a Director who used to put catsup on his sponge cake.

Well, I asked Madge to please sit down and tell me all about Tibetans. But any time I try to get her to keep me company, she can always think up some excuse to get away. So she said Clyde needed her out at Universal to autograph his Fan pictures.

But before Madge left she made the suggestion that, if I would try to read a book, I might be able to put my mind on something. And that was how, just as Skip always says, Divine Order gave me an answer. Because as soon as Madge left, I called up a place I have passed for years, driving to the nightclubs on the Strip, but I never dreamed of entering, called "Browser's Nook." So I asked for Mr. Browser, but it turned out his Nook is run by a wonderful boy named Vernon who helps pick out the book for you and told me on the phone that for years he had wanted to meet "la Bell Huntriss" (which in French means the Beautiful Effie Huntriss). So I told Vernon about deciding to read and he asked me, "Do you want to read for fun, dear, or for self-improvemint?"

So I told him to not send anything with plots in it. Because a person who has had to read as many film plots as I have, reaches a stage where reading can almost make you gag. So then I told Vernon about expecting the "Little Mouse" and I said I might as well improve the minds of both of us while I was at it.

And Vernon said he would "go through his stock with a fine tooth comb and dance right over to the house with them." So I invited him to take luncheon with me at my bedside, because I could tell from his dialogue that Vernon would never cause those deteckatives to even cast a glance inside my bedroom.

Well, in almost no time, Vernon arrived with a whole armfull of books. And we hadn't even started our Chop-Suey before I found out that he was very, very well-read. So I really dreaded when it was time for him to go back to work and leave me alone with all those books.

But after Vernon left, I started to read a book called *The Story of Madame Curie,* the eminent Pole who led such an extra-ordinary Love Life with her own husband and also got herself played by Greer Garson and discovered Radium. But when Dockie Davis came in that afternoon to check up on my condition, he reminded me they have already discovered Atomic Energy which is better. So I didn't bother to read all those pages about the Radium. Because things that are written outside of Hollywood always place the emphisis on the wrong thing. For instants, in Hollywood we realize that those Scientists keep right on discovering better and better things all the time, but emotions like Madame Curie had for Monsieur Curie can never be improved on. So when we made the Movie of it, we placed the emphisis where it should be.

So, the next book I read was called *Waldon,* about an economical man by the name of Thoreau who lived in the woods on the roots of a plant and considered it was just as thrilling to save money as other persons do to spend it. So I sent his book to Morrie as a joke and wrote in it, "How would you like to handle this Author and take out your ten per-cent in pine cones?"

And the next book I started to read was by a girl of Russian extinction called Marie Baskirkseff who led a Love Life which no Board of Censures would ever pass.

And I am sure the Johnson Office thanks their lucky stars she led it years ago, before Hollywood could be blamed for the whole thing.

So I called Vernon up and told him that as long as I was reading that sort of a book to send me some books about Hollywood. But Vernon said there was a dearth of true books about Hollywood, so why didn't I write one myself? But I told Vernon I would have to decline, because I was not sufficiently educated, on account of not having passed the Fifth Grade. But Vernon said that any author who went past the Fifth Grade had already passed the mentality where they could explane the phenomium of Hollywood.

So I laughed and envited Vernon to come over and have luncheon with me. But Vernon said he couldn't leave the Nook alone, because his Assistance was home sick with the flu. So then I decided to buy "Browser's Nook" so Vernon could neglect it. Because it only cost $30,000, and I have never discovered any kind of a man at such a reasonable price, to say nothing of having all those books thrown in with him.

But when I called Morrie up to ask for the check, it seems I owe the Govermint six hundred and fifty thousand dollars back Income Tax, from the days when I had another Business Manager who was more carefree than Morrie. So I told Morrie we could charge "Browser's Nook" off my Income Tax, because I needed to read it for Reference. But Morrie said if I wanted to read anything for Reference he would send me over a Biography he was going to buy an option on, that would be a good Film for my Come-Back when I can get to work again.

So the book was intitled *The Biography of Susan B. Anthony* and the thing which made Morrie feel that her Life had a Great Theme was a Scene where Susan B. walked down the Main Street of Rochester, New York, on election day and declared that the Govermint of the United States was in the wrong. And Morrie felt that, if the Script Writers gave it the proper emphisis, it might be applied to the modren Income Tax. Because Morrie said that my Fan-Following far out-numbered Susan B.'s, and if I could only swing them into action, it might bring back Capital Gain for everybody.

So I read the Book, and to say I became enthused would be putting it mild. Because Susan B. was the first roll anybody had ever considered me for that was not based on my personal apeal. And her costumes would be so realistic they would throw the entire Production on my ability to really act.

So when I called Morrie up to tell him how grateful I was, he was more cordial than he has been since the "Little Mouse" first came between us. And I was so thrilled to think that I had something defanate to put my mind on that I called up one of my Script Writers, who is a famous lady authoress, and asked if she could run right over to the house.

But that was where I made a mistake. Because I had forgotten about the quarrel she and I had on the last Script she wrote for me, where I had to play a scene with a child actor who not only had a lot of very sympathetic dialogue but was also supposed to be a cripple. And any Star in Hollywood can tell you what a great task it is to steal a scene from even a healthy kiddie. But when one of them is also a cripple, I defy even a

Star who can act, like Bette Davis, to surmount such an obsticle.

So the quarrel I had with this Authoress was over a scene where I had to say "Good-bye forever" to this cripple that I had raised from the time I picked it up at an orphanage when it was a baby. And in this Scene, my dialogue was to tell the cripple to be brave and not to cry. And the cripple's dialogue was to say, "But I can cry *inside,* can't I?" which would naturally start any audience dampening their handkerchiefs.

So, naturally, I had to go to my Producer, Bernie Koltz, and let him know the authoress had written some dialogue that was out of character for a small child and should belong to me. And I also asked him to tell Miss Versham to write me into the Script as the cripple and give the kiddie back the use of its limbs.

So my suggestion really flabbergasted Bernie, because he said it was the idea of a Genius. For up to that period, cripples in the Movies had been on the order of Lon Chaney in *The Hunchback of Noter Dame,* or John Barry More, when he played the repulsive aspeck of *Dr. Jekel and Mr. Hyde.* But to have a cripple like me would be Revolutionary because it would focus Audience-Attention on my Form in a way no Board of Censures could lay a finger on. So Bernie sent for Miss Versham and ordered the switch made in cripples, which she was enfuriated when she had to do.

But what made Edna Vaughan Versham go right on rankling after the picture got released was that the Box Office proved I was right. Because the picture broke every known Box Office Record. And in the scene where the Miracle took place and I recovered the use of my limbs in order to get out of bed and make a Bee-Line for Georgie Raft, audiences all over the civilized Globe went into a quiver. (Which only goes to prove that where there is a choice between a cripple kiddie and a cripple that has Sex Apeal, the Publick makes its own selection.)

So I should of remembered the dificulty I had with that authoress and sent for one of my more sympathetic writers. But my nature never retanes a quarrel and besides, my other writers were all men who have been pretty much in love with me for the duration of the shooting. And I don't think the "Little Mouse" ought to get exposed to thoughts of that kind until after it gets born.

So when Miss Versham arrived, I told her about Susan B. and how thrilled I was over my first chance to portray a Roll that was mentol. But Miss Versham started to cast aspersions on my acting ability by asking if I would try to play Beethoven's Sonata on a tamboreen.

Well—I hated to be unhospitable, but so long as Miss Versham started out by not being nice, I asked her if she thought an authoress ought to try to write vialent love scenes who had never got closer than ten feet in their lives to a vialent lover? So she asked me to tell her what was wrong with her love scenes? So I told her they were wordy.

Well, then Miss Versham decided she had better change the subjeck, and she started to attackt Hollywood as a place where unreality was allowed to entertain the masses. But I reminded Miss Versham that in the olden days the masses had to think up fantomes, like Goldylocks and Santa Claus, to idolize, so why isn't

32

there a lot more reality in idolizing persons that actually live and breathe, like Lana Turner and Humphrey Bogart, and, in addition, provide a great deal more variety.

So I asked Miss Versham, since she dissaproved of Hollywood, why she didn't go back home to Connecticut and try to entertain the Publick by writing her own Communistic idears, which irk them. And the only answer she could make, was that the only way she could earn enough money to keep her vast estate in Connecticut, was by working in Hollywood. So I had to ask her what was either brainy, or even Communistic, about *that*?

So then Miss Versham started to become sarcastic and said my Susan B. Anthony would probably be a great success, because the Motion Picture Publick would confuse the passionate love that Susan B. held for the Female Race with the intimate details of a Star that has had as many romances as I.

Well, then I lost my temper and told Miss Versham that anybody who starts to look for that sort of thing in my Susan B. is going to be dissapointed. Because my Standards are so high that the first thing I require out of any man is for him to say he respeckts me, even if our romance is all over in a few hours.

And I told Miss Versham how wrong it was for her to insinuate my feelings are not Sacred, just because I have had to go through one dissapointment in men after another. Because deep down in my heart I have always cherished the dream of attaining my Ideal, who is a sort of a combination of Clark Gable (for Manliness) and Gary Cooper (for being Difficult to Attain) and

Tyrone Power (for Romance) and Orson Wells (for Genius) and Fred Astaire (for Gracefulness) and Victor Mature (for being Well Built) and James Cagney (for Thrills) and Charles Boyer (for Experience) and Darril Zanuck (for Power) and Jose Iturbi (for Musical Composition) and Bing Crosby (for Vocal Accompanyment) and Roy Rogers (for Heroism) and Ben Hecht (for Dialogue) and Errol Flynn (for Shocks) and Inga Swansen (for Variety) and the Four Marx Brothers (for Laughter).

So Miss Versham said such a Pearl of Perfection could only exist in some vulgar Hollywood Filmplay. So that's when I told her how wrong she really was. Because he exists right in the Medalion Studio and he is a Film Cutter named Jimmy McCoy.

And Jimmy is far more important than any Star on the Lot, for every time we Stars express something incorrectly, he can take his sizzors and snip us out of a Climax that every department in the Studio has worked itself into a frenzy to acheeve, and replace it with an Insert of a dog, or a baby, or a railway train, in a manner that improves the Dramatic Impackt and leaves we Stars without a single leg to stand on.

And Jimmy McCoy has learned such a lot about acting that whenever he makes a remark, his Timeing is faultless. So every new Director that comes on our Lot naturally discovers Jimmy McCoy and offers to make him a great man in Hollywood. But Jimmy only

 Mommy's first serious roll had several diferent dimensions, caused by portraying a cripple who was born with Sex Apeal.

34

laughs and says Walt Disney proved the best man in Hollywood is a Mouse.

And the only girls at the Studio who are able to boast of any success with Jimmy McCoy are the miriads of secretaries and both of the manicures. So I told Miss Versham how the tradgedy of we Stars is that we can empress every man in the World, except the men who are worth empressing. And when we develop the first wrinkle that is too deep for the Cameraman to eradicate by shooting us through Burlap, we have to register at Central Casting Office, for extra work at ten dollars a day. And then all our Relations, and the Firm Friends we have accumilated through the years, have got to depend on their Social Security.

Well, hearing so much real truth about Film Stars made Miss Versham so uncomfortable she finally left in a state of Como, which is the case of everyone who ever tries to run down Hollywood to somebody like I, that really understands it.

But after she left here, I started worrying about those deteckatives once again. For the only other person who could of sent them must be Lester's wife, and if it is, she might make it difficult for me to follow Dockie Davis'es instructions, to try and have my Mouse in Piece and Quiet.

CHAPTER 3

Well, last week things finally took a turn for the worst. And Sunday was the worse day I've had out of Clyde since we got married. Because he had to stay home all day to prevint catching larengitus on account of the rain. And he finally became so desturbed over Inga Swansen that, not being a very good actor, it broke through all his attempts to act casual. But by bed-time, the rain finally stopped so it was safe for him to go out. So he told me he thought it would show me more consideration if he went to bed in his own suite and didn't desturb me by learning all that stuff out of Shakespeare and getting up at the crack of dawn to get out to the San Fernando Valley and shoot it.

So Clyde kissed me good night and told me not to thrash around, or get up, or come to his room because it might harm the little neucleus of our family life together.

Well, I didn't want the Mouse to know we were being

deserted, so I took a double dose of sleeping pills. But every time I dozed off, I kept seeing Clyde, in a Process Shot, diminishing until he was only a speck in the distance, with the "Little Mouse" squeeling "Daddy—daddy—daddy!" So then I would give a start and wake up.

And finally I got out of bed and tipped-toed into Clyde's bedroom to see if maybe I had done an injustice to him. But I hadn't, because Clyde hadn't even taken the trouble to rumple his bed. So I tipped-toed back, but I never went to sleep again and by morning I began to wonder if my sleeping pills couldn't be bettered.

So I put through a call to Bunny Ambrose on location in Sun Valley to ask what kind her doctor proscribes. So Bunny said she got hers from a one legged Jazz Trumpet Player named Gimpy Delane. And she said his pills work like a charm and are not habit forming, because Gimpy has used them for over ten years and wouldn't think of getting along without them. So Bunny said she would send me some by Air Male. But I got to thinking it over and decided not to take them. Because ten years might not be a "habit" at Gimpy Delane's age, but it would sure be a long period in the life of an unborn baby.

So I called up Gloria Trent and she said hers work quite well, but I found out she uses Dockie Davis'es too. So it probably means my metabolism has reached the end of any influence Dockie's pills can have on my own particular nervous system.

And when I called up Sylvia West, she told me hers were satisfactory, only she has had to keep increasing the dose, until now she practically has to make a meal

38

out of them every night before she goes to bed. But I told Sylvia I didn't think it was a good idea for my "Little Mouse" to go to sleep on a full Stummach. So we had a good laugh and I hung up.

But the trouble with that kind of laughter is that the pendilim is enclined to swing backwards and leave a Star feeling even more depressed—especially a Star that has "a Little Mouse in her trap," as Clyde used to say before he lost his sense of comedy over Inga.

So, to put my mind on something more constructive, I picked up my *Susan B. Anthony* and started to work on a conception of her that would even prove to Jimmy McCoy, in his Cutting Room, that I know how to really act. But when the maid brought my breakfast tray in, with the morning paper opened up, as usual, at Louella's collom, the first thing I saw was a headline that the *Biography of Susan B. Anthony* had been boughten by Sam Goldwyn who was going to emport Helen Hayes to Hollywood to portray my roll.

So while I layed here, clutching the pillow to try and keep from hystericks in order to proteckt the "Little Mouse," the phone rang. And it was Clyde who called up to tell me he didn't tip-toe into my bedroom in his pyjamas when he got out of his own bed, because he was afraid he would wake me up. But he told me to just relax and expect him home when he got there, because he had found out that Beverly Hills was the wrong environmint for Shakespearian study, so from now on, he was going to do it in a motel on the San Fernando Boulevard.

Well, I meerly agreed it was a good idear, for I had learned a long time ago that it only harms Clyde's self-confidints to let him realize I know what he is "up" to. And then I phoned for Dockie to come over and give me something to quieten my nerves. But while I was waiting for him I kept getting more nervous, and I didn't like to call the maids, or even the Butler, because their only contacts are with Madge who hires and fires them every week or so, and I never like to make a confidence out of meer strangers.

So what I finally did was to call Lester up at home and take the risk of his wife answering the phone. But when I got their house, the Butler said that both Lester and his wife were down at the Los Angeles Police Station, and at that momint Dockie was coming in, so I hung up without asking what they were doing there.

Well, Dockie gave me an injection that quietened my nerves and then he asked me, if by any chance, I had something more on my mind than he gave me credit for. So I broke down and told him about Clyde and Inga.

Well, then Dockie said that one of the chief dificulties of practising obstetericks in the Film Capitol is trying to keep we expectint Film Mothers cheery, because we have become accustomed to such lovely, warm scenes about Motherhood while at work on our Sound Stages. And then, when we try to carry them over into our Private Lives, we generally find ourselves in the midst of some Cold War with some husband like Clyde, or the

Your Mommy's conception of "The Woman in Black" brought Sex into the lives of hum-drum people all over the civilized globe.

contrary with somebody like Artie Shaw or Errol Flynn who are too hot to handle.

So finally Dockie gave me some new kind of sleeping pills and told me to be more cheerful, not only for the Mouse's sake, but to prevint adverse Box Office publicity against my Sex Apeal until the time came when I could let it speak for itself, by attending nightclubs in person with Howard Hughes, in a form-fitting evening gown.

Well, Dockie finally left and, in order to cheer myself up, I started to glance over the *Examiner*. And I soon discovered the reason why Lester and his wife were down at the Police Station. Because in a headline, clear across the front page, it said that Little Linda Carter (who is the daughter of Lester's present wife by one of her earlier husbands) had suddenly been kidnapped at the age of fourteen.

Well, the lives of all us Film Stars are so full of cataclisms that we are constantly on the verge of something terrible, but just the same, I become stunned each and every time it occurs. And this time, at least, Dockie's injection had caused numbness to set in and ease the shock.

But while I layed there, wondering if I couldn't do something nice for Linda's Mother, to retaliate for her present husband's sweet friendship to me every since we became divorced, I was dazed to see Lester merging through the door. So I thought, at first, it was a meer hallucination. But it turned out to really be Lester, in person.

And when I asked why he wasn't with his wife at such a time, Lester said that she was at home with Linda,

42

who had been picked up, safe, driving her car alone, on the way to Mexico. For the "kidnapping" had only been a scare and Linda had dissapeared because she was trying to run away from Hollywood.

Well, Lester said he hurried over here because he knew I must be in trouble, for I had never phoned him at his house before, on account of Gracie being such a vialently jealous temperimint. So I told Lester how I had got hysterical for fear I might loose my Mouse and had phoned him when I hardly knew what I was doing.

So then Lester set down on my bed in the purest friendship, and said he wanted to warn me about the dangers of Motherhood in such a controversial spot as we Film Stars live in.

And he went on to tell how Little Linda had always been a problim. Because her Mother had been so crazy about her, from the time she was born, that she used to rush home from the Set without even getting out of her make-up. But when the Baby was a few months old, Gracie's visits began to produce convulshions. For Little Linda would take one look at her and squall. So Gracie finally had to go to a Psychoatric to find out what was wrong.

Well, the Psychoatric said the trouble was caused by Gracie showing up at home, one day, in the make-up of a Bell of the Civil War, and the next day she'd be in a Bunny Rabbit outfit. So he told her to stop switching characters on the Baby and arrive at the nursery every day in the same roll.

Well, from then on, when Gracie finished work, she'd get into a pair of her own cute little shorts. So Linda seemed to think her Mother was her own age and, clear up until Linda went to school, they used to play, just like two Babies together.

But after Linda started school, she began to hear about her Mother's highly publicized Sex rating in Films, which started to confuse her. So Gracie tried to explane and say her Sex Apeal was largely trumpted up by the Publicity Departmint, and only existed in the minds of a few million of her Fans who loved her all the more for it.

But it seemed Gracie misunderstood the issue at steak. For the thing that was cutting Linda to the quick was something which took place every day, when the children assembled in the yard, at recess, and sang a lyric one of them had composed, which said,

> *Gracie Kay is corney,*
> *Gracie Kay is corney,*
> *Linda's Ma is corney*
> *Yah—yah—yah.*

Well, Lester said that not even their Psychoatric was able to figure out a Mother's reply, in Hollywood, to the aquasition of being "corney." But he told Gracie to send Linda, at once, to some other institution. And since Linda's real father had come from an aristocratic Pasadena family, Gracie was able to get her excepted by a very exclusive Pasadena Private Boarding School.

So the day before Linda had to enter it, Gracie sent her to the Beauty Shoppe to get her hair lightened, and a fresh permanint, and her nails done in a new shade from Max Factor. And then, the next morning, Gracie dressed Linda in her best party dress, and told her to remember her manners, and to always be on the lookout for opertunities to drop a curtsy. For Gracie had learned Linda how to do a curtsy that was practically a saallaam.

Well, Gracie couldn't drive to school with Linda that day because she was in the midst of shooting a big Bee-Bop sequence at the Studio, but she had boughten her a cute, cromium Cadilac Sports Roadster and Linda started out alone.

So that was how Linda, before she even entered school, had already broke their rules against platinum hair-dye, permaning waves, red fingernail polish, party-garmints in the class-room, and conspictuous transportation. And then, when Linda stepped into the office of the Head Mistress, she not only curtsied to the Head Mistress, but she also seezed the opertunity to drop a curtsy to the Head Mistress'es pet Poodle.

Well, Linda realized something was wrong the momint the Head Mistress told her they had suddenly found out they didn't have any unfillfulled enrollemints, so they would have to cancel her aplication and send her back home. But poor Little Linda couldn't bear to be disgraced again, so she went out of the office broken-hearted, and got in her Cadilac and started to leave Hollywood forever.

Well, while the tears were streeming down Mommy's face, in sympathy for Little Linda, the phone began to ring. And when I took off the receiver, I heard Gracie asking for her husband, in an angry voice. Well, butlers always tell wives in Hollywood that husbands aren't there, so Gracie finally hung up. And then Lester started to wonder how Gracie knew where he was at, and to also worry about Linda's home-coming being ruined by a jealous rangle. So before Lester left, he told Mommy to not feel bad in case something happened to my Mouse, because it might only turn out for the best if I never had one. And I hated to contradict him when he had only tried to be kind, so I didn't say a word.

But after Lester went away, I layed here all day long, wondering if he could be right. And I started to ask what I had to give my Mouse anyhow, except the absints of a Daddy and a large bill for back Income Taxes.

And then my mind got to dwelling on poor little Linda Carter and I begun to think how unfair everybody is to Hollywood. For I'm sure that none of her father's family ever broke any rules against cosmeticks in that snobby Pasadena School, but they sure broke the rules of the U. S. Govermint when they refused to go to jail for becoming wealthy in a famous Oil Scandal.

And then, little by little, it began to dawn on me that there was something very vital I could do for my Mouse. Because, while I'm laying here, I can write a book that will explane to everybody in the world the real truth about we Film Stars, so that no matter how high my Mouse rises on the Social Scale, or how much education it absorbs, Mommy's book will make it proud of Hollywood and I. And before I finally dozed off, I had become so optamistic I didn't even care whether Dockie's new pills worked or not.

And this morning the only thing to prevint me starting the book at 9 A.M. was the lack of a pencil in the house. So I phoned Vernon and told him I was going to follow his suggestion after all, and write a book that would change everyone's adverse opinions about Hollywood and turn the world into a more understanding spot to raise my Mouse in. And Vernon was so delighted he said he would bring over some pencils and paper right away.

Well, I layed here waiting for that stationary with more day-dreams for my Mouse than I have had since that night in a cabin on Bear Mountain when I first mentioned the idea to Clyde of becoming parents. Because at that period, Clyde and I were in the throws of a very vital Production, where I had a sexy roll that was supposed to ape Claudette Colbert in *It Happened One Night*, while Clyde portrayed a ruggid type who wanted his wife to only be a woman. So Clyde was as madly in love with me as I was with him, and the thought of a Little One to perpetrate it seemed like it would last forever. But that's what always happens.

Well, Vernon finally got to the house with a box of pencils and some large yellow pads and sevral books that he thought might give me some hints on how to do it. And I was so excited over the idear that I never felt a single pang when Vernon said,

"Well, I've got to run along now and dig up twenty copies of *Susan B. Anthony* for Sam Goldwyn."

For I had not only forgot my greef over losing Susan B., but I had also forgot Clyde's forgetfulness. And I realized that forgetting him had been as great a relief —if not even greater—than the relief I felt when I first really knew I had got him away from Carmen Dolores. For now I have my Mouse to care about.

Well, as soon as Vernon left, I took a pencil and tried

47

to decide how to start, which seems to be the hardest thing about a book. But when I glanced at a couple of 2 books Vernon had brought in (which are both entitled *Life and Letters*) I got the inspiration of putting my book into the form of a Mother's letters to her unborn Mouse.

CHAPTER 4

Dear Little Mouse,

When you are born you are going to find you are in a spot which is abt to always be misunderstood. Because, from the very beginning, the problms of Hollywood have been peculiar. And, way back in the old days when it first began, Hollywood was so far from civilization that, after a person got to the end of the Los Angeles Street Car Line, it still required a long walk through the dust before you reached the only known building, which was the Hollywood Hotel.

And before the Hills of Hollywood became a solid mass of stucco apartmints, they were mainly covered with Sage-brush and weeds. So the only reason the Films came here was to avade the heavy winter weather on Broadway and find the Sunshine which formed a requiremint of the old-fashioned kind of a Camera.

49

Well, in those days, even after reaching Hollywood, your only reward was to incounter a groop of Middle-Age Couples from the Middle-West, who came to the Hollywood Hotel every year to occupy a chair on the veranda and rock their winter away in Piece and Harminy.

And then all-of-a-sudden, those Early Day Film Actors swooped into that Hotel and provided those Middle-Age Couples with more diversion than they had ever dared to hope for, at their age. Because the California Sunshine did the same thing to those Film Actors that it did to those Middle-Age Couples . . . namely rejuvenization. But to take a groop of Middle-Age Middle-Westerners back to their early teens was one thing, and it was something else to do it to Actors who never realize their age at any period.

So it was small wonder that those early Film Actors, who had left their New York lodging house in a blizzard, and suddenly bursted into the Golden Sunshine, found their spirits reaching a new high. And almost overnight the Hollywood Hotel, which was noted for Peaceful Atmosphere and Western Hospitality, was forced to install a Bouncer. And it was only a question of time before the elderly Lady Proprietoress had to institoot a system of evictions.

But those early Film Stars soon found a means to combat it. Because that Proprietoress was so near-sighted she couldn't distinguish male from female and sometimes when she tried to break up some festivity, like a game of strip-Poker, a whole roomfull of revellers of several diferent sexes would claim they were meerly some of the "boys" holding a "Stag Smoker." So she would beg pardon for the intrusion and withdraw.

And many a Star that got evicted by that Proprietoress found it quite simple to go out the Main exit, and chat a moment on the veranda, with some smiling Middle-Western occupint of some rocking chair, only to re-enter in full view of the Proprietoress and check into the same suite, with the friendly assistance of both Staff and Guests, who were having more fun than they had ever had before in their whole life.

And the most momentis eviction to ever take place through that historic Lobby happened the night a famous Film Star got married to a wealthy society gambler during one of the Thursday Night Get-Together Dances (which had been instigated before the advint of Actors, when some sort of an impetis was required to get guests together). Well, that night the Bride and Groom retired up the Grande Staircase to the Bridal Suite at 11 P.M., but before the clock struck Mid-Night, that Silent Star was evicted down the Grande Staircase by the Bride-Groom himself, forming the Publick conclushion of a marriage that was never to be resumed and a Mystry which has never yet had any solution. For even today, when somebody tries to ask that Bride what happened that night in the seclusion of that Bridal Suite, the query is shunted off onto the subjeck of Hindoo Poetry, which is the pass-time she uses while she's waiting for her Come-Back.

But the Star who held the All-Time-Record for the largest number of evictions was the world-famous Dawn Dayton. Only Dawn has become much more conservatif today for she now holds the job of hostess in the Lady's Room at the Medalion Studios, where she loves to complane about the lack of freshness in the Lady's Room air, and gets her thrills out of playing Camille for the benefit of a Carpenter on the night shift.

But in the old days there was also an Intellectual Set at the Hollywood Hotel, led by the famous Best Seller known as Eleanor Glynn, where the highly popular Authoress layed on the floor, on a Tiger Skin Rug, and ixpounded occultism. And it was at the feet of Eleanor Glynn that the Greatest Siren of Them All (who was renouned throughout the civilized globe as Ileen McCabe) learned to express the intensity required to become the well-known "Rag and a Bone and a Hank of Hair" who brought relief to the hum-drum lives of normal people all over the civilized globe.

So now Ileen McCabe has a job with a Firm called the "DOGGIE'S BROWN DERBY" and drives an automobile in the form of a Derby Hat, with Ileen delivering dog dinners, in a bright brown unaform with gilt epolettes. So sometimes Ileen runs in to see Mommy when she is passing by. For Ileen feels very deeply about Motherhood and she even gets emotional over every expectint bitch along her route. (And this is as good a place as any to learn my Mouse that when "bitch" referres to the canine Sex, it is never a four-letter word.)

Well, back in those days of Silent Films, Hollywood, like any newly publicized spot, was abt to attrack the lawless elemints who were forced to flea from trouble

 The part of "Crystal Carruthers" in Adrift on the Rio *was cute, but she didn't augmint Mommy's stature as an actress, much.*

in other spots. But when they reached here, they were stopped by the Pacific Ocean from going any further, and so a few of those lawless elemints drifted into the Films. Because in those days the only schooling required to become a Film Actor was for somebody to step in front of a Camera. And once when the Immortle D. W. Griffith stopped a scene he was shooting, to count noses, he discovered every profession known to man or beast, except a wheelwright.

And then sometimes the Silent Films themselves had a tendincy toward Law-Provoking. Because there was no necessity for Actors to learn any lines so, with time on their hands and nothing to put their minds on, and the California Sunshine to relax their inhibitions, they used to drift into idle habits. And at one period the entire Mercury Studio, in a body, was forced to go across the Border into Mexico and shoot their comedies on a sand-lot for six months, because they suddenly found out that one of their extra girls happened to be under the Legal Age of 18 according to the Civil Code of the State of California.

And so every time something occured along those lines, the Publick would inveritably escribe it to "Sex." But Mommy wants everybody to remember that the persons who committed those affronts in the early days received their Home-Influence far from Hollywood. But now Hollywood has had a second Generation born and bread here, and inculkitated with our own ideals. So among we Film Stars of today, there is very little of the ixtravigants which sprouted up when high salaries first began and there wasn't any Income Tax. And when, for instants, Baby Peggy, at the age of three, rode down Hollywood Boulevard in a Sky-Blue limousine, personalized with a solid gold name-plate and with mineature lace curtains at the windows. And Tom Mix ordered a jeweler to slice the top off a large diamond and form it into a watch crystal for the wrist-watch of Mrs. Mix, his Cow-Girl Bride. And the fabilis Hope Hampton ordered Our Savior's "Crown of Thorns" to be copied in real diamonds to wear in one of her Productions.

But today we Film Stars belong to our own exclusive Country Club, or direct our thinking along Political Lines, or practise Oil Painting, or become Authors and Authoresses (like Mommy), or maybe buy and own our own Picasso, so that decorum has taken the place of showmanship.

And Mommy wants everybody to realize that the Publick has always placed a smirch on Sex which is not put there, under no circumstances, by Hollywood today. Because we feel that the most Sacred Things in Life are the result of Sex . . . like Motherhood and Babyhood, and Mommy's "Little Mouse." And Our Scripture Itself says "Men cannot live by bread alone."

So Hollywood recognizes the fact that throughout the length and breath of Our Land, a great portion of our Publick does not enjoy sufficient Sex Life in the Home. So it is obvious they are the nicest type of persons, who form the backbone of our very Nation, and they have to depend on the Films of Hollywood to get it. But contrary to the type of persons who think that Sex is an ugly thing, Hollywood today, without exception, makes it pretty.

And Mommy believes in the Great Law of Unity

which teaches that, when people hold their Thoughts very, very strongly, the Thoughts materialize and Thinkers ultimately receive what they demand. And so, Little Mouse, I feel that all the concentrated Thoughts of all the unfill-fulled Men in the whole World have coagulated to produce your Mommy.

But in addition to the idealistic side of Hollywood, there is another side, which sometimes makes demands on everybody's couradge. For, when we Film Stars find ourselves in trouble, Hollywood seems like a red hot Volcano. And every time a Star doesn't get an option picked up, Hollywood seems more like some ice-cold, deserted glazier. And sometimes it even litrally has an actual earthquake that shakes the buildings down. And even buildings that don't get levelled by some Act of God, no sooner get built than the Realtors commence to tear them down, which sometimes encludes a large slice out of the very Hills of Hollywood themselves. So the result is that we do not have any permanint Spots to place the affections on, like San Francisco with its Golden Gate, or the Sacray Coor in Paris, or the Old Kentucky Derby. And the only historic spot we have is the Hollywood Hotel. But it is dificult to grow sentimental over a spot which is only occupied today by economical tourists from Kansas and Illinoise.

And so Mommy doesn't want her Mouse to expect to love Hollywood with Sex in its heart, the way local citizens love "Frisco," or "Texas," or "Paree," or "Old Kentucky," or "LaBell France," or the "Emerald Aisle." Because the first requiremint of any Love that's going to be warm, is that the person has first got to relax. But Hollywood is so unpredictible that even a Long-Term

Contract doesn't lead to relaxation. And so all of we Film Stars, and the Loved Ones who live off our salary, and the Members of the Technical Unions that depend on entertaimint, and the Voice-Coaches and Dancing Schools and the employees of Glamor-Spots and Night Clubs, and the Agents and Shops dependint on our Nation's Box Office, all feel like they are standing in front of some Juggernought with a tendincy to hit-or-run. And whenever there happens to be a lack of perpetual California Sunshine, there can be a tendincy toward gloom.

But on the other hand, Little Mouse, no matter what anybody says against Hollywood, always remember that you have got to respict it. Because Hollywood has turned the tide of Civilization of the whole, entire World.

And one time, when Mommy took her trip to Europe, it made me feel very proud, when I arrived at Paris, to note all the Mademosselles wearing the Horn-Rim-goggles of Hollywood. And to see all the stores on the Grande Boulevards advertising "Genuine Hollywood Sports Garmints." And, in the dress salons of the Hot Cuture, to see all the little French Modelles wearing their sleeves padded to assimilate Mussels that were over six thousand miles away, on the shoulders of Greta Garbo.

And when Mommy was returning back home on the boat that time, I became friendly with a Danish Professor who was on route to a Philasophic Convention at Harvard. So Mommy told him I would love to make my Films slightly more artistic for the European taste, and asked him to suggest what I could do. And this Philasopher's reply was,

"Nothing!"

For he told Mommy that the Whole of Europe owed Hollywood a great Intellectual Debt because our Films had come to its rescue at a time when it had grown tired and skiptical. But he said to know that creatures like "Effie Huntriss" were actually living, breathing and glissening with spangles in the California Sunshine, removed all their Intellectual snobbry and forced them to believe in the invincibel reality of Fairy Tales.

And so, Little Mouse, Mommy wants to squalsh, once and for all, the criticisms people make that the entertainment of the Film Capital is meerly childish. For doesn't even Our Scripture Itself say, "Accept you become as Little Children, you shall not enter the Kingdom of Heaven"? And while a lot of people, outside the Film Industry, are being childish in a very deliquent manner, by dropping Iron Curtains and Atomic Bombs, we children of Hollywood, at worst, are meerly naughty.

And your Mommy believes that when the time comes for all of us to harvist our reward, and Our Creator has to judge the deliquent "children" who run the Govermints of this World and we "children" of Hollywood, the Gates of Pearl are not going to resimble the entrance to the United Nations so much as they will the corner of Hollywood Boulevard and Vine Street.

Chapter 5

Every time that Dockie Davis pays a call, he always gives Mommy the self-same proscription, over and over, which proscribes a Normal Life with Harminy and Piece of Mind, to assure the safe arrival of the Mouse. But yesterday turned out to be the kind of a day that Dockie says I should never, under no means, have. Because early this morning, when the Sunshine was streaking through every slat at the window, and I felt maybe the day was going to start off cheerful, I picked up our copy of *Cinema Daily* and noted an alegation which said that it was Lester's Wife who was hiring those deteckatives to shadow me.

Well, it naturally depressed me very much to think that Daddy hadn't cared enough for Mommy to put deteckatives on me. But I took a benzidrine and begun to feel more optamistic. And then I began to try and foamilate a plan to get my Mouse its Daddy back. And

I decided that if he and I could only have one more interview, in the Piece and Quiet of the Home where we were happy for a little while once, it might bring us together again.

And then, just like a Response from Unity, I began to hear Clyde moving around in his bedroom. So I very carefully got up, and put on a more dressy negligee, and slipped into Clyde's suite.

But it wasn't Clyde, however, because it was his vallet, Andy, who had come to pick up Clyde's Collection of Pipes that he left behind when he walked out on us. For Andy told me Clyde had just been selected as a "Gentleman of Distinction" so he needed his Pipe Wrack to pose for the Add. (And Clyde looks so manful, holding a pipe in a photograph, that he would just as soon be shot without his hair-piece.)

Well, Andy's company is always cheering, so I asked him to set down and tell me what "The Boss" was up to these days. But all Andy would say was,

"Oh, the usual thing."

And when I tried to get Andy into a corner, all he would say was,

"Miss Huntriss, you know about as well as I do what's usual with Mr. Babcock."

Well, then I asked Andy what he would think if Clyde and I went back together again. So Andy said,

"If I can stand him, Miss Huntriss, I guess you can. Because I ain't even obligated."

So then we had a laugh together and Andy said he'd better go, because Clyde would soon be arriving at the Studio. And he loves to start his day off cheerful, by hearing Andy make commints on how well-built he is, while he helps Clyde dress. So I told Andy to run along and keep the Boss'es complexes from getting inferior. But then Andy said,

"Maybe Mr. Babcock ain't got any inferiority complex, Miss Huntriss. Maybe he just plane *is* inferior."

So we laughed again. But when Andy started to leave I suddenly got an idear and asked if he would go to the Studio and tell Clyde I was keeping his Pipe Wrack at my bedside, as a keep-sake, and wouldn't part with it to anyone but him.

Well Andy realized how dearly Clyde would love to hear such a defanate complimint from anybody, so he thought it was a good idear too. But while Andy was carrying Clyde's pipes to my bedside, he happened to say,

"Miss Huntriss, have you ever got a good whiff of this Pipe-Wrack?"

And the odor to which Andy refered to, was true. So I told him he could put it out on the balcony and, as soon as I heard Clyde's car pull up, I'd bring it in.

But as Andy was going out, he stopped and said,

"You better keep an eye on that Pipe Wrack, Miss Huntriss, or this California weather might get at it."

And Andy was right again. For Clyde's pipes mean more to him than anything, except his denture (for which a man can never feel any pride of possession). But Clyde loves to vaunt about his pipes in Publick, and constantly does. So I promised Andy I'd keep a close tab on the weather.

Well, after Andy left, Mommy layed here trying to foamilate the best way to make Clyde fall in love with me all over again. And I realized how dificult it was going to be, because the very fact that he had been able to overlook those Pipes of his since he went away, goes to prove how absolved he must of become in Inga Swansen.

And starting to visualize the way Inga Swansen looks, began to make me afraid it would take a much stronger Sex Apeal than Mommy has to lure your Daddy away from her. For there are two varieties of "looks" among Film Stars. And one kind is the type which gives the men a very informal attitude, and even causes Radio Comics to bounce gags off us (like they do off your Mommy and Jane Russel).

And a few Stars, like Olivia De Haviland, are beautiful, without being pretty (on the order of Mona Lisa, or Venus D. Milo), which meerly produces idealistick thoughts in the men.

But Inga Swansen's looks, at one and the same time, are both beautiful and pretty, which is a very invidious combination. For most of Inga's features are so Classic that they fill the onlookers full of awe. But, on the other hand, she has eyelashes that are so over-length no Painter or Sculpture would dare to desecrate their Work of Art with anything so flashy. So Desecration cancels the Ideals, and the combination becomes tantalizing beyond restraint to men and boys and (they even say) other persons.

Well, I finally put the dark thoughts of Inga out of my mind, but then another kind of dark thoughts took their place. Because Mommy knows Clyde so well that I could sense the very momint he began to worry over the Publicity that will acrew as soon as the Mouse arrives. For it will inevitably bring up a reference to two children he had by a wife of his boyhood, who are so grown up, now, that they're in Colledge at Boston.

And I begun to remember how the momint we were certain there was going to be a Mouse, Clyde started to pass cigars around and say, "Have your cigar *now*, and jump-the-gun on the little Monkey," until everybody (except Mommy), got sick of the whole subjeck of Fatherhood, encluding Clyde himself.

Well, going over all the problims Mommy has to solve before I can give my Mouse a Normal Home Life, finally started to make me shake so hard that I had to call up Dockie Davis. And he said to take one of my phena-barbitel tablets, and, if I didn't get any affect, to take another. So, after one tablet didn't stop the shaking, Mommy took another and it worked so well, I soon begun to drowse. And Mommy only waked up when I began to be conscience of the pity-patter of some rain.

Well, lissening to the rain was very sootheing for a while. But, as I started in to slowly concentrate, I commenced to realize the storm was pretty brisk. And then I thought instinktively of Daddy's Pipe-Wrack. But as I was jumping out of bed to rush out to the balcony and rescue it, your Daddy himself stepped in from the balcony holding his Pipe Wrack, dripping, in his hand. (For he had come in while Mommy was asleep and looked for his Pipe Wrack at my bedside, and when he failed to note it, he had searched and found it in the rain.)

Well, all I could do was stand here, trying to think up some sort of an apology that might sound like a complimint. But the words never came. And then Clyde

63

began his usual tick-tacks of blameing me when he feels guilty, and doing it louder and wordier than I can.

And then, as if I had not heard the details so many times I can't even concentrate on them any more, Daddy began telling how that Particular Favorite Pipe of his was made out of Genuine, Imported Meer Chum, that had been carved by the Swiss from one big, single piece of Meer.

But when he thrusted it at Mommy, in order to prove his point, his favorite Pipe started to come apart where the rain desolved the glue. And insted of getting angry at the Pipe Shop, that had made a doop of him, your Daddy begun to naturally take his greevince out on me.

So he said that when Andy had told him how I always kept his Pipe-Wrack close beside me, it made him feel he was so vital to the happyness of others that he came right Home to hear me tell it to him in person. And he said I might even of been able to patch things up, but when he saw his prizeless Meer Chum being rained on, he knew we could never live in Harminy any more.

And then Clyde went on to say,

"Effie, I might as well let you know that, these last few weeks, I've been secretly going through the most serious Crisus of my life."

Well, I didn't want to tell Clyde I had guessed all about Inga, because he would only take it as a slur at his subtlety, of which he is unordanately proud of. So in order to not upset him, I meerly asked what the Crisus was, this time.

And then Clyde went on to say,

"Effie, perhaps this isn't the momint to tell you, but the day I realized your interest in your child was becoming just as keen as your interest in me, I knew our marriage was not the perfeck mating I had hoped it was."

Well—Mommy realized that nothing could stop the break from coming now, so I carefully crept back into bed, to make my Mouse as comfortable as possible for the ordeel. And Clyde lunged right ahead and said,

"I suppose every chap in the world dreams of one day finding his perfeck mate. And I have never claimed to be any diferent from all the other, every-day-sort-of-chaps in the world, have I?"

So I gave Clyde the answer he required, and said, "No."

And then Clyde went on to say,

"Mind you, Effie, I don't wish to deny you've been charming, much in the manner of a child. But after all, I am a mature man, with a man's deminsions. And, I am also an Artist. And, as such, I have my obligations to a Publick."

So then Clyde stopped and took a piece of paper out of his pocket, that was a page from a Calendar some Fan sent him last Christmas, with a motto on every page that has turned Daddy, this year, into a Reader and a Scholar. And he handed it to me so I could see for myself, the Printed Proof that everything he ever wants to do is Right. For it said,

"Let each become all that he was created capable of being; expand, if possible, to his full growth; resisting all impedamints, casting off all foreign, especially all noxious adhesions; and show himself at length in his own shape and stature, be these what they may. Carlyle."

Well, while I was reading it, I started remembering back to when Daddy's Nick-Name for Mommy had been "Kitten," which is a far cry from being termed a "noxious adhesion."

So while I tried to keep my lip from quivvering, Clyde started to nervously pace the floor, like he always does when he subconsciously tries to overlook he's in the wrong. And he went on to say that he had found somebody who was capable of making him reach the highest Peak his Stature was capable of attaining. And his voice naturally took on a tinge of pride when he announced the "Somebody" was the fabilis Inga Swansen, and that the thing which had brought them together was no less than Shakespear.

Well, I politely tried to give Clyde the empression his blow was a surprize, but then I tried to remind him how, when he first started learning his roll, we had been very happy together while he layed here, learning Shakespear, by reciting it to me all night long.

But then Clyde reminded me that, while he was studying it with me, he never even considered his roll had any opertunities. But he began to find out that Shakespear was greater than he had ever realized, as soon as he started playing with Inga.

Well, then I asked Clyde to please sit down and lissen for once. And I tried to make him understand it was meerly Sex Apeal that was doing it to him.

Because, laying here in bed alone has given Mommy time to think, and to realize that all we Stars, who base our private Life on Sex Apeal, and all our Script Writers, who base our Scripts on the same thing, have led not only Hollywood but the whole Nation astray

66

by makeing Sex seem like it was something unusual.

So then Clyde asked me who I was, to suddenly take a stand against Sex Apeal?

So then I told him that perhaps Morals were more authentick when preached by persons who had had to learn them the hard way, like I. For I told Clyde that, if my own Personal apearance had never taught me anything else, it had sure taught me that Sex doesn't last forever.

So I begged Clyde to realize we were both going into a New Phrase, and ought to try to live a Life where our Mouse could grow up in Harminy and have respeck for both its Mommy and Daddy. And I asked him to please not confuse our Mouse by having a divorce that would only be the sign of a week character.

Well, whenever Clyde feels subconsciously guilty, he can always think up some defence that even Mommy can't deny. So he said,

"Was Julius Cesar a week character? Or Napoleon?"

Well, Mommy had to say,

"No."

And then Clyde said,

"Well—Cesar divorced! So did Napoleon! And Douglas Fairbanks!"

And then he started to go. But he stopped in the door long enough to say,

"Effie, in all fairness, you can see that our Life together would only be one continuous jangle. So, if you want to have your child in Piece, I'd best bow out."

And then Daddy left. So after that there was nothing I could do for my Mouse but take a few more phena-barbitels.

Chapter 6

Well, all last week, Little Mouse, the house begun to get very quiet, which is always the case as soon as it stops being noisy. For the momint Lester read that his Wife had placed deteckatives in Mommy's summer house, they suddenly dissapeared, so he must of made her stop it.

But then the house begun to get a little bit too restful. For the momint a Star lays off, there's no motivation for the telephones to continuously ring, and the place to be over-run with persons who want a job in your picture, or with Visiting Vondeuses from the stores, or Reporters, or Ghost-Writers, or the Camera Men who want to snap you in the Piece and Quiet of your own environmint. And Morrie has even made Mommy stop receiving any Fans, who sometimes remain loyal for months after you quit. Because Morrie says the South-land is a pray to Gangsters (who love Sunshine just as

69

much as anybody else and are enclined to use your Fan Clubs as a "cover-up" to get into your Home and use it for their "base" of operations). And personal friends can seldim run in because in Hollywood the distance is so far from one spot to another.

For the most outstanding shock that Tourists ever get is to find out that "Hollywood" is meerly one of unnumerable other spots, which we Citizens term "Hollywood" as a "cover-up" for the whole accumilation. And the largest spot is not Hollywood at all, but Los Angeles which, in Spanish, means the City of the Angels who wear a halo of smog, which is a combination of smoke added to dust and flavored by the verious chemicals of all the ever-growing industrys. For Los Angeles is surrounded by hills, which takes on the form of a gigantic coffee cup, with Los Angeles as the dregs. And since it can never be drafty in the bottom of a cup, smog accumilates daily, to the great benefit of a large body of Eye-Ear-Nose-and-Throat Specialists.

And next to Los Angeles, the second largest section is Hollywood, itself, which contains several Large Studios. And any surprize that a person fails to get in one hour on Hollywood Boulevard doesn't exist.

And adjacent to Hollywood are all the famous residential locations, like Beverly Hills and Brentwood, which are Garden Spots full of Film Stars Homes. And any Tourist who steps into any Super-Market can see the most glamerous girls in the world, dressed informilly in their shorts, trundling their groceries around in little wire wickets.

But the most exclusive location of all is Belle Air, where every house is a Large Estate, occupied by some

70

Star, or Magnate of Films (or other industrys). And Belle Air is so wide-spred that pedestriams could take endless walks through the beautiful foliage, if there were any paths. But the long distances of Hollywood have addickted people to transportation, so that they have largely lost the use of their limbs. And members of the British Colony (like Aldous Huxley) who cannot be discouradged from walking on the highway by the swift momentim of the traffick, are frequintly stopped by the Police for having no visibil means of transportation, and arrested for pedestriamism.

And there are so many other Locations, Towns and Communities in the vicinity of Hollywood that even our old Settlers seldim know where they're at, while the meer Tourist never does find out. And the Mystry is intensified after dark, because the Publick Official who designed the Street Signs worked along the lines of an optical allusion, by placing the Name of the Street in front of the Lamp Posts, which acheeves a Black-Out.

But with distances so far away from one another, it is very dificult to be neighborly. For instants, if Bunny Ambrose wanted to pay Mommy a call, it would take her an hour to get here from where she lives, at Toluca Lake. And Bunny is working now, so she's too busy. And the Stars who are not busy don't like to pay visits, just to sit around and trumpt up excuses why they're not working. While Sylvia West, who only lives in the next block, hates to run in, because she just signed a new Seven-Year Contract and Sylvia has such a sweet nature she hates to flaunt herself in Mommy's face under the circumstances of me not working.

But while Mommy has been laying here in Piece and

71

Quiet, the atmosphere has anyhow been ideal for Reading, Writing and Arithmetic, which Morrie has made me take up. Because Morrie feels that if I write my checks out, in person, insted of having Madge do it, I will be automatically forced to read them. And it will provide me with a fright which will turn out, in the end, to be only beneficial. For the momint Mommy's salary check for $4,500 stopped coming in every week from the Studio, the figures on the stub don't do anything except dwindle. So today when Morrie came in and saw that the last amount on Mommy's stub reveeled only $883.40 to keep the house running until the Mouse has arrived, and Mommy has got another contract and made my Come Back, he said that Daddy would imediately have to take over the sole brunt of the housekeeping.

Well, then there was nothing for Mommy to do but let Morrie know about a pre-numptial agreement I made with Clyde that absolves him from the expenses that acrew out of Matrimony. Because Clyde has a disilusionmint with Matrimony that dates clear back to his First Wife, who he married (as a boyhood prank) in Boston, when he was only a Salesman, going from door to door, selling Refrigeraters. But it wasn't long before Clyde's success gave him the huntch that his personal attraction went far beyond any salesmanship of meer Refrigeraters. So he decided to get out to Hollywood.

Well, the Alimony that the Divorce Courts of Boston granted that first wife of Clyde's, had not been too devastating. But the momint he became a Film Actor his Wife took a trip West and got it rectified. So, even

72

before Clyde got to be a Star, he was paying more Alimony than should be required of any normal man.

But, as the time went on, and Clyde reached the full Flush of Stardom, he found he was having to work so hard that he never had a free momint to enjoy the Tribute of his Fans. So he began to think it would be very invigerating, after a long, hard seige at the Studio, to always have a Film Fan handy, right in his own Home, twenty-four hours a day. And he was so impetuous about getting her in there, that he never learned the existince of a California Statue against Matrimony, which decrees that every husband and wife auto-matically earns half of each other's salary, by Law, without ever turning a hand.

Well, the day finally came when Clyde's Second Wife ceased being a Fan, and got ahold of a Lawyer, who brought that California Statue to Clyde's attention. And then Clyde was dragged into the Los Angeles Courts, where every Judge and every Member of the Jury has either written a Scenario (that has been rejected) or else tried to become a Film Star (to no avale). So when it comes to making a Decision against some Star, no Book is ever large enough to throw at them.

Well, the momint the Oposing Counsil started to recount the large Salary Clyde received, for doing nothing more irksome than make love to the early version of Joan Crawford (when she specialized in playing Wayward Daughters), the Judge and Jury naturally started to compare it with the small incremint they earned in the hum-drum surroundings of their own unglamerous employmint. So the Alimony they granted

Clyde's Second Wife broke all previous records for unearned incremint (and is still being extracted every week by the Court before Daddy's Check ever leaves the Studio). And the episode left Clyde with a vialent phobia against ever doing it again.

But when it came to his Third Wife, Clyde felt safe, because she was a Star who earned a lot more money than him. And, according to the California Statue, half of it legally belonged to Clyde, although this time he was so in love, he never even dreamed of trying to collect it.

But when it came time for their divorce, Clyde's Third Wife rushed to the office of the Best Lawyer in California and got there ahead of Clyde, who had to be contented with the Second-Best.

Well, unfortunately for Clyde, it happened that the Judge had only not written a Serial intitled *The Cases of Blackstone,* but he had also enformed all Studios that he was available to star as Blackstone in it, himself. And the very day Clyde's Case came up, that Judge's scenario had been turned down by the last Studio in the entire rostrim of Hollywood Film Corporations. So he awarded Clyde's Third Wife half of everything his First and Second Wives didn't get, while the two smartest Lawyers in California took the remainder.

But when Mommy finally finished telling your Daddy's troubles to Morrie he spoke up and said,

"Be that as it may, Effie, you are intitled, by Law, to

 In Orient Express *my conception of Fritzi Gabour, a well-known spy, got me mentioned for the Oscar once.*

half of everything he earns, after the extraction of Court Costs, plus the Alimony of his First, Second and Third Wives, plus the Upkeep of two Colledge Boys, plus the Fedral and State Income Tax."

And then Mommy was forced to tell Morrie that in order to win Clyde's consent to matrimony, I had had to sign a paper that repudiated the California State Law.

Well, when I told Morrie that, I could almost see the flecks of foam begin to form in outrage, at the corner of his mouth. And he said it was high time for me to drag Daddy back into the Courts again. But I told Morrie that I firmly intended to keep that paper Sacred, in the hopes that I can get my Mouse its Daddy back. And then, with his ixpression growing grimmer by the momint, Morrie said that if I wanted to remane at the mercy of Clyde Babcock and a bank balance of $883.40, I would have to get a more half-witted manager than him to handle my career.

So I told him to go ahead and go. And Morrie walked to the exit in a rage and only stopped long enough to remind Mommy that the Golden Days of Hollywood is over, and contracts have grown to be so short and scarce they take your breath away. And, to add emphasis to his assertion, Morrie walked out and slammed the door.

And so now, with Morrie gone for good, the Mouse and I can live in Piece and Harminy without having to lissen to unpleasant subjecks like the $650,000 dollars Back Income Tax that Mommy owes. Because Dockie Davis says it might be dangerous for the Mouse if Mommy ever has to worry.

CHAPTER 7

Well, Little Mouse, in order to compleetly understand all about Hollywood, a person has got to first understand Sex Apeal. Because it is one of the many things
that the largest number of people know the least
about (which Mommy learned when I called Vernon
up, to ask if he would send some books over on the
subjeck, by some of the other Authoresses who were
born Sexy).

But Vernon said the only Items he had in stock was
a book of Poetry by an Ancient girl called Sapho and
a Modren Authoress called Lorelei Lee. So he sent them
over. But the girl called Sapho writes as if she was a
"Wolf-in-Sheeps-Clothing." And Miss Lee's Book is
more about finances than emotions. And then, when
I called Vernon back, to complane, he said he could
flood Mommy's boudoire with books that go into all the
details of how men feel in the presents of Sex Apeal
(like a book called *The Eve of Saint Agnes* by Keets or
a play entitled *Venis and Adonis* by Shakespear). But

the opasite point of view, telling how girls who have got it, feel the presents of men's reactions, has not been very adequintly covered. And Vernon finally said,

"You've got the Field all to yourself, dear, so sharpen your pencil and go ahead."

Well, I guess the best way to start is by telling my Mouse how, from the time Mommy first became available for romance, I have yearned with all my Heart to be loved not *because* of my Sex Apeal but in spite of it. Because when Mommy was about Fourteen, and my baby-fat began to dissapear (except in the spots where it began to augmint), Mommy's Form sometimes failed to bring out the best in Passers-By. And sometimes the worst their Thoughts seemed to be, the more they seemed to find the words to express them. So Mommy was forced to lissen to very adult dialogue at a period when most children never hear such terms spoken audibly.

And Mommy wonders why men don't sometimes wonder if we girls don't get sick of that sort of dialogue, which depends for its emotion on a choice of words that, to begin with, are monitinous. And, in my own case, I sometimes feel there is more Sex in some casual remark about the weather.

But back in Kansas City where I grew up, there was always one spot where I could find the kind of Romance I had always dreamed it was going to be. And it was at the Bijou Motion Picture Palace, in Mommy's neighborhood. Because no matter how much Sex Apeal those Film Stars had, every man in the picture either reacted to it with gallantary, or if they didn't, they came to such a Tragic End that it was a sheer delight to witness. And

78

the enjoymint used to last long after Mommy came home and went into Day-Dreams of being held in respeckt by Walter Pigeon.

And then one Saturday Matinee, Mommy saw a movie called *The Little Minister*. And in this picture the Minister was so lacking in aggression that even a Gypsy Girl was forced to egg him on. And when the climax came, and this Minister finally gave in, he did it in a manner that took all the obnoxiousness out of Sex. For he only kissed her on the forehead, lightly, while his dialogue epitimized both gallantry and warmth as he told her she was "Bonny."

Well, as long as that Film played in Mommy's neighborhood, I went to see it (even when I had to extract the dime out of the money my Mother sent me out to buy the Groceries or the Meat with).

And then, at that school in Kansas City, something extraordinary happened. For one day a new Teacher appeared there, called Mr. Russel Sudbury. And when Mommy started to incounter him in the hallway, I began to wonder who he reminded me of. And then it suddenly dawned on Mommy who Mr. Sudbury resembled. For, although he was quite tall, his personality was almost identicle with the film version of that Little Minister.

And then something even more unusual happened. For one day Mr. Sudbury who taught Algybra (which was far beyond any class which Mommy ever reached) started to institoot a new Course that took in the whole Student Body, of Lessons in The Scriptures every Friday morning. Well, that first Friday morning, as Mommy gazed at Mr. Sudbury he looked so pure as

79

he stood on the Rostrim, reading the First Chapter of the Bible, that all he needed was a Light Effect on his pale red hair to assimilate some Saint with a Halo.

Well, Mr. Sudbury had worked out a Routine where every time we students learned a Motto from the Bible, we would win a Small Religious Card. And after we had won twenty Small Cards, we could turn them in to him for a Large Card. And on the day before the Easter Vacation, the Student that won the largest number of Large Cards would receive a Bible, that would be presented in person by Mr. Sudbury himself.

And so, every day, Mommy put in all my time learning Mottos from the Bible. And Mommy's diligence soon began to be rewarded, for whenever I incountered Mr. Sudbury in the Hallway or out on the Street, he started to pay me complimints on my proficiency.

And Mommy used to often have Day-Dreams about being alone with Mr. Sudbury, in some lovely out-door location. And our conversation would consist of commints on the Scenery and the Flowers and the Birds. And then, at the climax, Mr. Sudbury would touch Mommy lightly on the forehead and tell me I was "Bonny." After which, I would call Mr. Sudbury "Russel" and thank him.

Well, by the time the Easter Vacation came around, Mommy had broken every record for the accumilation of Large Religious Cards. So when I was allowed to walk up the isle, to receive the Prize Bible from the hands of Mr. Sudbury himself, Mommy's thrills could hardly keep within bounds. And after the Exercises were over, and Mr. Sudbury told Mommy to come to his own Private Class Room and receive his personal congratulations for all the Mottos I had learned, Mommy's heart was hammering so hard I almost didn't think I could bear the exsticy of stepping into such a 7th Heaven.

But Mommy had no sooner stepped into Mr. Sudbury's Class Room than he began to behave in the self-same way as those men I had always brought out the worst in. But I finally wrentched myself safely away from him and ran all the way Home and cried my heart out.

Well, when that Easter Vacation was over, and Mommy had to go back to school and incounter Mr. Sudbury once more, we used to turn our gaze away from one another. But Mr. Sudbury's face would get as red as Mommy's. And he looked so guilty that, of course, I had to finally start in feeling sorry for him.

Well, things went along the same, until that Kansas City School held our Fourth-of-July Picnic. And on the way to the Picnic grounds, Mommy happened to be in the same Bus with Mr. Sudbury. And he looked so mizrable that I begun to worry I was ruining the Picnic for him. So after lunch was over, and it came time to scramble into the Ferris Wheel, I got into the same cage Mr. Sudbury had chose, so I could tell him, while the Ferris Wheel went round, to not feel so bad about it, because I had gotten so used to that sort of an episode, it almost failed to surprize me.

Well, Mr. Sudbury accepted my apology, and then he spent the afternoon escorting Mommy through the Zoo with scientifick explanations of Wild Animal Life. But that night, when Mr. Sudbury ought to of been enjoying the Fireworks, he began all over again to feel

81

so horrowfied at his behavior that, to finally comfort him, Mommy underwent a Romance.

And from that time on, it began to seem as if Mommy has always had to accept men on their own terms. And even during the War, when I used to try and bring out the best in our Armed Forces by reciting a poem that told our boys how "the man worth while is the man who can smile when everything goes dead wrong," their whissels were so loud I could never get my points over.

And then on one momentis evening Mommy finally had the Ideal opertunity to meet a large Groop of men on my own terms. For I arrived at a Barrick full of soldiers, where I had to entertain them in a Black Out. So I begged Bob Hope to not tell the boys who I was in the dark, and to by no means mention my nick-name of "The Bust."

Well, Bob agreed, but without being able to see Mommy, those G.I.'s started yelling so loud for Zazu Pitts that I couldn't be heard any better than when the lights were on full. So the episode finally made me realize that any time I try to meet the men on my own terms, the result inveritably cancels out into nothing.

But as time goes on, I am learning more about Divine Order, and beginning to feel that Stars like Mommy are an Instrument in a Cosmic Design. For in every audience of every Movie Theatre there is a large majority of Girls who were born without enough Sex Apeal

 Your Mommy's first starring vehickle, The Nude Deal, *was produced before Mommy was well-known, or even blonde.*

82

to provoke the intentions of their Escorts. And so it requires somebody like us to supply the motivation by a systim of Remote Uncontrol.

Chapter 8

Well, every once in a while, Little Mouse, Nature does something to prove the Rule that good things come in threes. So that was what happened last week. And the first good thing was, on Thursday, when Morrie called up to tell Mommy he had no sooner walked out on us than he felt sorry and wanted to opologize. So he said he would like to come back. And I was very touched, but just the same, I feel he'd always be a disterbing elimint, for I am sufficiently psychic to read Morrie's thoughts, which will never be Harmonious on the subjeck of your Daddy, even if he holds himself in check. So I thanked him, but I said we were going to get along all right, and he could handle my Come-Back when the time came, so to not worry his head over us.

But when the second good thing came, it was miraculious. For the very same morning your Daddy called up. And, while Mommy layed here, quaking at the sound of his voice, your Daddy told me how upset he was our Marriage had not worked out to my advantage. And then he said he didn't like to earn the reputation of a Law Breaker, but he was going to vialate our Pre-nuptial Pact and present me with 12 dollars and a half per month.

Well, it was just like your Daddy to make the sum such a peculiar figure. For Mommy could close my eyes and see him, as he was wavvering between 10 dollars a month (which he was worried might make him appear to disadvantage) and 15 (which he couldn't quite bring himself to meet). So then he figured out how much Uncle Sam would allow him to detract from his Income Tax, after all his other deficits, and it worked out to be 12 dollars. But then generosity over-came your Daddy, and he tacked on the added fifty cents. And knowing him so well as I do made the tears come to Mommy's eyes. Because everything is relative, and for your Daddy to devote any amount of money at all to one-more-additional-wife, and do it of his own volution, almost puts him in the cattygory of a Saint.

But I told your Daddy to not bother, because if I ever needed anything, I could always phone him. But then he ensisted, for I guess he was afraid if I called him up, I might name my own figure. So I excepted and I had to smile, because your Daddy's foibles always hit my funny bone.

And then, that very evening, the third good thing occurred. For around ten o'clock Vernon stopped by, on his way home from the Movies. And as he was approaching our neighborhood, he began to deteckt that Mommy's help was holding a Mascarade Ball all over the lower extrimities of the House.

Well, Mommy had been lissening to their racket

every since Cocktail time. But they were White Help who can always be expected to give partys in your home if they feel its safe, while Colored Help, on the contrary, can't wait to get down to Central Avenue, where they know there's more fun to one square inch than in all of Hollywood combined.

And Mommy had had a feeling for several days that the Staff were also taking other Libertys. Because while I am confined to my Room, hints keep cropping up that the rest of the House is being denooded of brick-a-brack. But I was afraid if I mentioned it, the Butler would quit, and take the Cook and the Second Story Girl with him.

And I hated to call Madge and bother her about them, because Clyde keeps her hopping all day long at the Studio. For he is as touchy as any Famous "Golf-Pro" over having a large "Gallery" follow him around the Lot. So it's poor Madge's job to try and organize a gallery among Studio Personelle, to who no Film Star is ever any novelty.

And it isn't Madge's fault when Help turns out unsatisfactory. Because she has to except the recommandations they show her, which are from other Stars who are so frantick to get them off their own Premiss that they will screem their very praises from the House Top. (And Mommy has been known to write a recommandation myself, for a Chauffeure who's Driving Power was meerly an adjunct to Cracking Safes. So to get him out of the house, I was more than delighted to write, "Eugene is leaving of his own accord and our Home will never be the same without him.")

And the only Help that ever supplied me with a feeling of Security was a Finnish Cook called Helga. But one day Mommy offered Helga two Persian rugs and a new fur-trimmed coat I didn't have any use for. Because the coat turned out, when I got it away from the shop, to be unbecoming, while the rugs I had thoughtlessly boughten in Atlantic City, on a rainy day, at an auction, on the Board Walk, when I was alone. And it wasn't until those rugs got shipped Home to Hollywood, I realized I didn't have anything Persian to go with them. (Which teaches a lesson that there are more ways than one for a girl to get in trouble at Atlantic City on a rainy day.)

But instead of Helga grabbing those gifts (like all the other Help I ever have always do) she told me she couldn't feel at ease in any Home where there was such a lack of Thrift. So she quit her job and walked out, leaving the rugs and the garmint behind her.

And so Help are the biggest trouble-makers in Hollywood, outside of the persons we Film Stars have automobile axidents with. Because when the brush of your Car is as light as a feather, they can always sue for "Shock" and give a very legitimate performance of spasms. For, at heart, every Citizen of Hollywood is a competint actor.

Well—while Mommy had been laying here lissening to the Help giving that party, I couldn't help thinking of the day when I felt I had reached the very heights of opulince, because I was able to hire somebody to work for me. But inwardly Mummy has never felt as much at Home as I did in my small room at the old Cal-U-Met Hotel in Culver City. Because, without ever realizing it, I have always been subconsciously sure of what was going on in the kitchen.

Well, when Vernon peeked in the window Thursday night and saw Mommy's staff and their envited Guests draped in sheets as antient Greeks and Romans, he sneaked in through the servants entrance and bounded up the back steps to tell Mommy that revellery was all over the place. So he begged for permission to bound down-stairs and fire them.

Well, I thanked Vernon for his kind consideration but I told him that, with all their faults, they never miss a meal. And they serve Mommy with the same as they have, which is delicious when sufficiently warm. So for the Mouse's sake I have need of the nourashmint they pervide, and I had ought to keep them as long as the money holds out.

Well, then Vernon began asking about Mommy's Financial Statis. And then I quoted him the balance at the Bank. And then Vernon proved his Friendship over and above anybody that Mommy has ever met yet. Because, without any ulterior motivation, he offered to move right into the House and watch over Mommy during the hours he didn't have to be at the Nook. And Vernon said he could vouch for his Cookery and that he would bring along the Maid who did the cleaning at his Bungalow Court, who has never been near a Film Star, so she could be trusted.

Well, Mommy was delighted to except Vernon's kind offer, but by this time the party began to reach a New High, so Vernon decided it was best to call in the Police. And luckily the Help had never thought of cutting the telephone wires, so it was only a jiffy before the Riot

Squawd were breaking the front door in and putting a wet blanket on preceedings. And then they went through the Help's bedrooms and made them return every article that had been thefted from the House.

Well, as soon as the Police removed the Offenders and departed, Vernon's first thought was whether Mommy had had anything to eat. But I had, for on Help's day off, Andy always finds time to rush in sooner or later with a nice hot Tomali and an ice cold coke.

So Vernon ensisted on remaining at the house all night, as a protection for the Mouse against Mommy getting nervous. And the next morning, while Dockie Davis was here to keep me company, Vernon rushed over to his Bungalow Court and got back with the new Maid before Dockie had to leave.

Well—the new Maid Vernon brought in has turned out to be adorible. And she is also very talented. For one time, when Peoria was living at the City of the same name, she had a job with a lady who learned her how to Polychrome (by first putting paint all over something and then rubbing it off again). So besides doing the house-work, Peoria is going to Polychrome the whole place, up-stairs and down, in all the verious different tones of gold.

And Peoria can hardly wait to finish the house-work down-stairs, to rush upstairs and set on Mommy's bed, all day, and keep me company. And the only trouble is that she keeps wanting to know why the Mouse's Famous Daddy isn't anywheres around.

Well, Peoria only arrived from Illinoise a few weeks ago, and, to her, Hollywood seems like All-the-Fan-Magazines-in-the-World Come True, so I would hate to crush Peoria's allushions. And when I explane Daddy's absints I always speak in the vernackular of the Fan Magazines and tell Peoria how Clyde Babcock happens to be one of those Stars who lives and breathes his roll so conshenshusly that, on leaving the Sound Stage, he can't throw off his mood. And I told her how the roll he is creating now possesses certain destructive aspecks which might be dangerous to Our Mouse if he should ever happen to come Home.

So Peoria said,

"Do you mean Mr. Babcock is playing a skunk?"

Well, in the phrazology of Peoria, he is. So I had to say "Yes."

And Peoria's commint was,

"My! My!"

But when I told her the plot which Shakespear concockted for your Daddy's Script, she was even more astrounded. And I think myself that no huntched back cripple ought to make a propasition to a Widow during the Services of a Dead Husband she had dearly loved.

But when I told Peoria how that Widow began to enjoy this Cripple's insidious behavior with full Audience Parcipitation, she finally came down to Earth and admitted Shakespear certainly knew Human Nature. But then she wanted to know what Shakespear would say was the reason your Daddy didn't come home. And while I was trying to figure out a pleasant way to tell her I was releeved to see Vernon merge through the door and interrupt.

Well, Vernon had drove over to Morrie's office during his lunch hour to pick up my Book Keeping Accounts. But Morrie was off at some studio, so his Secretary called Mommy up, to find out if she had ought to let Vernon have them. And when I told her "Yes" and said that Vernon was living with me now, the shrug of Hazel's shoulders was almost audibble. So Mommy was afraid that, sooner or later, I was going to have to hear about the matter from Morrie himself.

Well, last night after dinner, Vernon told Peoria to sit over in the corner and be quiet and then he and Mommy went to work on my expenses. But when Peoria heard Mommy mention the amount I owe Uncle Sam, she said, "Miss Huntriss, that Uncle Sam of yours ain't nothing but a great big pimp." So Vernon had to send her down-stairs to her Polychroming.

Well, Vernon finally compleeted a Budgit which he thinks may hold out until the Mouse arrives, by augminting it with Mommy's Credit and his own salary. But he had no sooner gone down-stairs to wash the dishes than Morrie called up and started poking fun at the "Romance" betwixt Vernon and I. But I soon let Morrie know that there was nothing to laugh at. Because having Vernon around the House has given Mommy such a feeling of releef that I have already noted a deterioration in the consumption of my phena-barbitels.

And I reminded Morrie that Modren Life can become very complikated and there are times when a boy like Vernon is the only gap to fill a breach. And I also told him that Nature generally knows what it is doing. For when I had said to Vernon that I didn't know how to ever thank him, a lump had come in his throat. But Vernon tried to speak cazual when he remarked,

92

"Think nothing of it! This is the nearest I'll ever come to having a Baby."

So Morrie had to opolagize and hang up.

CHAPTER 9

Well, Little Mouse, to wake up and hear Vernon down in the kitchen, whisseling while he concockts delicious surprizes for my breakfast, is such a lovely way to start the morning that Mommy is able to keep cheery all day long. And when evening comes, it is the best of all. For Vernon sets with Mommy and we dwelve into the gossip of the day, which he picks up from verious Browsers in the Nook. Or else I read Vernon what I've written, and he makes commints or gives Mommy his suggestions.

So last night Vernon said he thought the next thing I had ought to tell was about my Background, before Mommy's Career started to foamilate, and to let people know the requiremints necessary to become a Famous Film Star. So this morning, while Peoria is busy doing the down-stairs, Mommy is going to lunge into the Story of my Past.

And the first thing I can remember is when I was very small, and my own Momma and I used to continuously travel, trying to catch up with my Daddy (who I used to call by the Nick-Name of "Dadda"). For Dadda was addickted to a roving life of rideing Race Horses and trying to keep away from Momma. So we were always on his trail, following the Races from Tan Foran, to Belmont, to Jamaica, to Saratoga, to Epsum Downs and Etc.

But whenever Momma and I were left alone together, her mind was inveritably off on Dadda. And it was plain to see she was secretly suffering from his evasions, for her thoughts and conversation would be "foggy." But they weren't much better when we cought up with him. For she never felt at ease in Dadda's Racing Set, who talked in the vernackuler of the period and, in edition, were highly amuseing.

But betwixt Dadda and I, there was always a very warm intente. For, although we were careful to never mention it audibbly, we both shared the same fear that poor Momma was congenitly a bore. So I would never blame Dadda for running away, although he and I were idylistickly happy when we were together. For Dadda had learned me to ride Horseback almost before I could walk (which came in very handy when I had to, later on, ride Horses in a picture). And when we were galliping around the Tracks together, we both were safe from Momma boring the ears off us.

Well, many persons earn the reputation of boredom without ever learning of their afliction. But I felt that Momma decteckted hers. Because no sooner had she made a mistake in conversation than she began to realize, too late, that she had made it. So she seemed to always remaine more silent than boresome persons generally do.

And there are also persons who can make a "slip" and remain cute while doing it. But Momma never could. And I can remember a party that a Trainer Friend of Dadda's gave one Summer Night in the Receiving Barn, at Reno, where they built a dance-floor and did a new dance known as "The Big Apple." So when I mentioned it I called it, by mistake, the "Great *Big* Apple," and everybody laughed and Dadda hugged me. But when Momma, later on, made the same identicle mistake, everybody winced and Dadda didn't hugg her. So I guess one of the great mystrys of Life is Personality. But Momma had been born without it.

Well, one time when I was about eight years old, Momma and I had trailed Dadda acrost several States, and lost the scent in Kansas City. So while we were waiting for news of him, Momma got herself a job at the same Firm where she was working the day she first met Dadda. For it was an Establishmint that made outfits for Jockeys, and she first fell in love with Dadda while she was fitting him to his Silks.

So Mamma felt that working for that Firm made it easy to contackt the members of the Raceing Fraternity who went through Kansas and could give her news of Dadda. And we settled down in the first real, furnished cottage we had ever been able to rent. And since Momma's job was to meerly do the "finishing" on outfits, she was able to work at Home. So she used to sit with one eye always out the window for Dadda's return (even when we were hearing roomers that he was in Astralia, or Singapore or Cheko-Slovakia, or England).

But I was too accostomed to missing Dadda to continuously greeve for him, the way Momma did. So at Kansas City I was in Heaven. For I began to realize that trying to find Dadda at one Race Track after another had caused me to always subconsciously worry about what was going to happen to us next. But to wake up, morning after morning, in the same spot, and immediately recognize the same furniture, and know that Momma was safely earning the rent-money herself, gave me a feeling of Social Security I never even knew I had been missing. (So that is the kind of Security I am planning for my Mouse. And in order to make our Home seem as if it had always been permanint, I am going to fix the attick up with a whole jumble of old fashioned mimentos, which Skip Norton has promised to sneak out of the Prop Departmint for us.)

Well, at Kansas City Momma paid me 10 cents a week to pull out the bastings. So for many a week I spent all of it at the Five-and-Ten-Cent-Store, buying nick-nacks for the interior decoration of my own room (encluding a large dried bouquet of pink Pampis Grass, and several Colledge Pennints from assorted Institutions, and a Picture-Frame to go on my beaureau, made out of real Oriental Sea Shells, with a Snap Shot of Dadda holding his arm around me, just after he won the Preekness).

Well, there were children on the sidewalk in front of that cottage, who I got to know personally and played with for the first time. And finally, at the suggestion of the Truant Officer, I started going to school, which I didn't mind so long as the other children were in the same predicamint.

Well, after about eight years had gone by, and I was

sixteen, who should show up one day but Dadda. And when I answered the Door Bell and saw him standing out there, I could hardly believe it. For he was the same cute, well-built, stylish little Dadda, who had his picture on my beaureau, with the same dark Sun-Tan that always augminted his blue eyes. And the only thing I had forgot about him was the expensive smell of the Cologne he always used, which came back in a rush the momint I whiffed it again.

But Dadda couldn't believe his eyes, because I looked so diferent. For at the time he escaped us I was a meer Roly-Poly, with facial feetures that were undistinct. But in the meanwhile I had got slenderized and grown to be even a little bit taller than Dadda.

Well, I will never forget that first day we three spent together, with Dadda telling about all the adventures he had had, way off in Turky rideing for a Turk who must of been very popular, for Dadda never spoke of him without calling him "Atta Turk."

So after Dadda got tired telling his own adventures, he asked Momma what I had been "up to" since he went away. Well, Momma didn't want to make him feel sorry he had come Home, so she was careful to only tell him the good things and never mention my Report Cards. (And, of course, she didn't mention Mr. Sudbury, because I had never told her about him myself.)

And then, as usual, Momma began to try to find out Dadda's plans and whether or not he would let us accompany him. So Dadda told her he would be rideing next at Aquaduct, and it would be better for us to not trail him, but to stay Home at Kansas City where I could remane in school.

So of course Momma bursted into tears and I could tell that she begun to blame me as a detramint, even though Dadda and I both understood (subconsciously) that if he couldn't of blamed me, he would of thought up some equally good excuse for leaving her. But he anyhow tried to tell her that, now he was rideing in the U. S. again, he could keep in touch more closely with us.

Well, it turned out that Dadda had come back with a large Turkish Bank Account. So the next day he got it translated into money and took Momma and I on a Shopping Spree to Emer-Bird-and-Thayer's. And Dadda bought me dresses which made me begin to view my Sex Apeal with pride and not alarm. For everybody in the Dress Departmint (and even some of the Shoppers passing through) stopped to pay Momma and Dadda complimints on the way I looked (which made me realize that Sex Apeal in expensive clothes can often turn disrespeck into plaudits).

But I had started to note, however, that Momma was feeling a lack of personal attention. So they happened to be interoducing a new Fashion of dresses for "Mothers-and-Daughters" at the Store that day, and I thought it would make Momma feel more important if I suggested that she and I have two dresses which were both alike. But the momint we tried them on and looked in the glass, I could see a mistake had been made. For Momma's dress was so unbecoming that nobody would ever of thought we even belonged in the same family.

But that evening Momma and I got dressed up (in new dresses which were diferent) and Dadda took us to dinner at a Cafe where music accompanied the food. And a groop of Dadda's old cromies from the Track were there, with the fabilis Mr. Pendergast, who I never dreamed I'd ever see in person.

Well, Mr. Pendergast dearly loved to see a family out having their pleasures together, so he sent a Bottle of Champagne to our table and drank a Toast to me, acrost the room. And every man in his groop was frantick to dance with me, if Dadda would of consented. But he danced every dance with me, himself, in my new "Debutant" outfit.

And then, between dances, Dadda started to revise his plans for Aquaduct and said, after all, it might be a good idear for him to take me (and Momma) along with him. For he couldn't wait to see the repercushions I would make in Raceing Circles, sitting in the Private Box of his New Owner (with Momma).

Well, we stayed at that Cafe until early the next morning. But after we got Home, and I was laying in bed, fondelling the new platinum Wrist Watch Dadda bought me, and trying to not go to sleep for fear I'd dream he had never come back, I heard somebody creeping into my bedroom. And I wasn't afraid of a burgler, but just the same I had a very peculiar meloncolly feeling. So I quickly set up in bed and switched the light on.

Well, it was Momma. And she was bringing me in some breakfast on a tray, which was very unusual. And I soon found out my meloncolly feeling was psychic, for she started to say that I was in very grave danger. And then she went on to tell me that Dadda was no more my Real Father than she was my Real Mother.

And then she told me how she had adopted me from

a Strange Lady when I was only a few days old, because a Horse-Owner's Wife had told her that a Baby might cement her Home together and prevint her husband's frequint dissapearantses. So she said that when I failed to do it, she was afraid she began to unjustly blame me. But insted of trying to find me a good Home somewheres else, she still held onto me because she realized I was the only one in the family who never bored Dadda. And she always lived in the hopes that someday he'd get fed up with Travel and begin to take an interest in a Home.

But she said the look on Dadda's face when he gazed at me made her realize she and I could never have any Future with one another. For if I began to cement her Home together at that late day, it would be in a way that she could never bear.

So then I asked her if she thought I could maybe go back to my Real Mother. But she said that, sixteen years ago, when she first took me, my Real Mother happened to be in Transit, without any forwarding address. So they had lost track of one another.

Well, while I sat up in bed there, lissening to the news that I didn't belong to anybody, everything began to feel very unsecure again and strange, including the Pampis Grass Bouquet and my collection of Colledge Pennints, and even the Snap-Shot of Dadda and I, after the Preekness.

And then, while I was becoming more stunned every momint, she suddenly asked me if it had ever crost my mind to run away to Hollywood and get into the Movies.

Well, the mention of going into the Movies gave me a

sudden start, because I guess it had subconsciously been on my mind for a long while. So I asked her if she thought I could really do it. And she said that judging from my success that afternoon at Emer-Bird-and-Thayer's, and also that night at the Cafe, she was sure of it.

So then she put a big role of money in my hand, which she had taken (for his own good) out of her husband's wallit, and asked if I wouldn't like to start packing my lovely new clothes, so I could catch the earliest possible train in the morning, before he woke up.

Well, I got out of bed in a daze. And while she helped me pack, I hardly knew whether to feel lost, or excited, or sad, or even numb. For it was a pretty big wrentch to even think of leaving him, after all the plans we had started making to always be together at the Tracks. But I tried to stop thinking about him, and to put my mind on Hollywood where some day, perhaps, I would get to meet Joan Crawford, who was my ideal. And then a hopeful emotion would start cropping up, and I'd begin to feel as if maybe there would be some way to endure it.

And I was glad anyhow that she and I had never got closer to one another. Because, even with her being remote, I hated to think I never would see her again. But I didn't think that she'd have any squalms about me going away, until it was almost train time. And then she broke down, not with greef over me leaving, but with Self-Acusation over never having prepared me with any private instructions on my personal relations with the men. And she said that now, when I wouldn't have her around any longer for guidants, she would have to try and make up her dificiency by telling me The Facts of Life. But she was such a halty conversationalist (even on subjecks that were dull) that she became compleetly tongue-tide trying to discuss something entertaining. And I felt so sorry for her that I told her about Mr. Sudbury and said she needn't bother. And I was glad I told her, for it seemed to greatly ease her Conscience to know I was going off to Hollywood with some sort of adequint preparation.

Well, by this time it was beginning to get late, so she pervided me with my Bearth Certificite (encluding my Real Name), and then it was time to say good-bye. So I said it with a meerly formal handshake, because I wanted her to feel that I respeckted her resentmint and knew she couldn't help it.

But just as I was starting to go through the door with my baggage, she pulled me back into my old room and said there was one thing more I would have to do, in order to make things easy for her. And it was to forgive her for telling him, when he woke up, that I had taken the money out of his wallit myself and skipped off somewheres without leaving him a word.

Well, I would dearly of loved to have Dadda think about me at my best. But I had to remember that she had taken care of me all those years, when her Heart had not been in it, so I told her to go ahead and tell him anything she wanted.

And then I stealt past the door where he was laying sound asleep, and went out of the cottage which had been more permanint than any place I ever knew, and took a taxi (all by myself) and bought my ticket at the Union Station and got on the train.

But the Train had hardly got past the Out-Skirts of Kansas City when a wealthy looking, middle-aged man stepped up to me and said,

"I beg your pardon, but aren't you Spanish?"

So I told him I wasn't. And then he said he wasn't either. But he seemed to think that being mutually un-Spanish constitooted an interoduction, and set down.

Well, I had to politely endure him until he was eventually forced to go to the Wash Room, and then I quickly got ahold of the Conducter and got moved into a private compartmint. Because I felt I had gotten into too much trouble through men who were exciting to bother getting into it with someone boresome.

Well, I locked the door of that compartmint, and set there thinking about how quick Dadda would be leaving her again. And I looked at my platinum wrist watch and wondered what sort of a story she was telling him, that very momint, about me. (And I'm afraid she told him plenty. Because ten years later, after I had become a Famous Star, he rode the Winner in the Santa Anita Handicap. And I was the one who was regulated to put the Wreath of Roses around the neck of his Mount. But when I did it, he looked me over with the most glassy stare I have ever received from anybody [outside of women]. So while I stood there, knowing the thoughts that must be running in his mind, I began to feel as if I was really guilty of them and broke into such a vialent blush that it made the Technicolor Shots look faulty.)

Well, for the whole duration of that trip to California

I stayed in the locked compartmint of that car, meerly getting my nutrimint from the Bromo-Seltzers I ordered from the puzzled porter. And I kept right on thinking about Dadda and about her, and all the kids I'd played with for so long, and the Fifth Grade (uncompleeted). And I thought how, every since my Fourth-of-July Picnic with Mr. Sudbury, things had been very active and peculiar. So I kept saying to myself over and over, "This must be what people term 'living.'" And here I was, starting to descover all about it, for better or for worst, in Hollywood.

CHAPTER 10

Well, looking out my window in that compartmint, Little Mouse, I could finally see cactis plants as big as trees growing up in the dust, so I knew we must of reached the Southland. And when the famous California Orange Groves heeved into view, I could tell that Los Angeles itself must be aproaching. Because everything was just like the Fan Magazines had led Mommy to suspect, except there was a lack of California Sunshine. For California Rain was coming down in drizzles.

So finally the Train stopped at the Pasadena Station and I saw my non-Spanish Boy Friend get off, and be greeted by a non-Spanish wife of his own age. So I heeved a sigh of releef, for I had been planning to remane in my compartmint at the Los Angeles Station until he dissapeared.

Well, the Train fairly crept all the rest of the way and, although Pasadena is practically at Los Angeles, it seemed to almost take forever. And the nearer we got to Mommy's destinition, the more I started quaking from nerves and (I presume) an over-dosage of my Bromo-Seltzers.

Well, by the time the Train stopped, the Rain was coming down in solid sheets, so I had to open up my suitcase and get my old Rain Coat out, to protect my nice new outfit. And when Mommy was ready to get off, and looked in the mirror, I could hardly recognize my own self. For due to Mommy's restrickted diet on the trip, added to crying, and to not being able to sleep, my eyes had got deep circles and my whole face was red and puffy. So when I stepped off at Los Angeles I looked gastly and felt my very worse. But the Porter got me a friendly Red Cap who saw me to a Taxi Cab.

Well, there wasn't anybody I could turn to in Los Angeles except the Taxi Driver, so Mommy asked if he would kindly allow me to ride in the front seat with him and get his advise about what I ought to do next. So he was agreable, and while we were driving through Los Angeles, I told him my problem of wanting to break into the Movies.

But with Mommy's face all out-of-shape and Mommy's form covered by my wrinkled Rain Coat, I could see Joe didn't think my Career was abt to be very promising, although he was anyhow quite brotherly, and said he knew all about the Movies, because his present wife had come to Hollywood from winning the "Idaho-Potato-Queen-Contest" two years ago and she was now registered at Central Casting under the cattagory of Red-Heads-of-One-Hundred-and-Ten-Pounds-or-Less. And she could also Ice Skate.

So Joe said the most important thing was to "Put up a Flash" and that Mommy had better stop at the Beverly Wilshire Hotel if I had the money. So I told him to take me there. And then we seemed to be driving through the Down-Pour for hours, passing mile after mile of enormous sign-boards that were all advertising products of an edible variety (such as Cottage Cheese and Bake Beans and Doughnuts), which was very diferint from other cities, where other kinds of comidities are also featured. And when we finally reached the Hotel, Joe said he would call me up the next day to see how things were breaking. And he told Mommy, in his brotherly manner, to take it easy.

But when I got inside the Beverly Wilshire, the Lobby looked very large and very empty because when there's no Sunshine in Southern California, there's nothing to come out of your room for. So when Mommy registered I was still depressed and shaking badly. But I went up to my room and decided I had ought to anyhow eat something, so I picked up the phone and ordered the first meal I had had since that breakfast I had lost my apetite for, the night she brought it to my bed in Kansas City.

So then I took my bath in almost a State of Como, and by that time the Waiter wheeled in my Lamb Stew and Pie alla Mode on a table, and I ate all of it. And then Mommy fell into a deep slumber and I never woke up until I heard the phone ringing and heard some strange man's voice say,

"Hello, Effie, this is Joe."

Well, at first I didn't know who Joe was, or even where I was at, until he reminded me he was the Taxi

Driver. And then I found out it was the next day and I had slept for 24 hours.

So Joe finally said to Mommy,

"Have you made any mileage since you got here?"

And I told him I hadn't yet, but I guessed I had better start in.

So Joe wanted to know if he could have the job of driving me around the verious Studios, because he said there was quite a slump in the Taxi Trade. So I said Okay, and Joe said he would be there in an hour.

Well, I looked around the room and saw the California Sunshine streaming in and giving everything a very diferent aspeck. So I hopped out of bed to dash to the window and look out. And the view Mommy saw was so thrilling it made me almost forget about Kansas. For I noted that right acrost the Street was the fabilis Brown Derby Restaurant I had always read about. And every other building, in every direction, looked so bran new in the California Sunshine that it dazzled your eyesight and made me feel as if I'd never be able to get enough of it.

But then I started in to worry over my possible lack of acting ability, and wonder if I had anything to offer to the Movies. But when I went to take a look in the mirror I was stunned. Because the sleep had rested Mommy, and the excitement augminted my looks, until it seemed as if I looked better than I had ever looked before. So I ordered some Pan Cakes alla Mode and Coffee.

And then I took my shower and unpacked my gorgeous new Sweater-Outfit. And then I quickly ate breakfast and put on a copious Make-Up which would be suitable for the ocasion. And then I got into my Sweater (which I realized looked even more gorgeous after Mommy pulled it on). And pretty soon the phone started ringing, to say my Taxi was there. So I hurried out to the Elevator, to not keep Joe waiting.

Well, the Elevator Door was opened by a very pleasant Elevator Boy, who looked at Mommy as if he had suddenly had an electrick shock. And then he said,

"Say, where have you been up to now?"

So I asked what made him bring the subjeck up. And he said,

"Sheer urgincy."

So I thanked him for the complimint. And as he recovered his equalibrim and started the Elevator I asked if he would give me his advise as to how I could break into the Movies. So he took the Liberty of stopping between floors and said,

"Honey, all you've got to do is heeve into sight."

But by that time somebody was ringing the bell, so we had to preceed.

Well, when Mommy stepped out into that Lobby that morning, I would never of thought it was the same place I had entered that other morning in that Rain-Storm. For it was the Hour when everybody connected with the Movies was busseling to get to their Studio, and all the Tourists were stepping briskly starting out into the Sunshine.

And the Lobby of the Beverly Wilshire (at its best) is just like a Gold-Fish Bowl for new Screen Talent. So when I walked over to leave my door key at the Desk, I could plainly note that the Clerks deemed it an Event. And the attention I received when I went through that Lobby towards the Door made Mommy feel just like I was a Parade.

Well, when I merged out onto the Side-Walk, Joe was holding a conversation with the friendly Door-Man, who remarked quietly to Joe, on seeing Mommy,

"Pipe!"

And when Joe turned round to look, he reacted as if I was a Neon Sign that just flashed on. But I could tell from Joe's expression that he didn't recognize I was the same Girl he picked up at the Station, in a form-concealing Rain Coat. For when I stepped up to Joe and told him it was Effie, he opologized and said he was so busy looking at me, he failed to see who it was.

But then the trouble started. For Joe began to take the attitude that picking Mommy up had put him in the position of "Finders-Keepers." And he seemed to think that having me previously set in the front seat with him had constitooted a precidince. So to prevint hurting Joe's feelings I had to set up beside him again.

But Joe's intentions (even with a Potato-Queen-Wife) became so un-brotherlike that I had to finally threaten to scream unless he stopped his Taxi and let me get out and walk. So he had to stop it, and that was the end of Joe. (And incidintly, it was also the end of any brotherly interest from almost everybody that ever picked me up in Hollywood.)

Well, I got out of Joe's Taxi, and started to walk in the same general direction, for I knew I must be in the vicinity of the Standard Lot, which was where Joe had planned to start me out at. But even the most ordinary looking Pedestriam walking in Hollywood is such a novelty that every driver going by stops to inquire why a person is doing it. So Mommy was forced to finally except a Lift. But I was very careful to select a Driver of my own Sex who kindly dropped me at Culver City in front of the Standard Lot.

Well, the Man at the Main Gate told Mommy I would have to get a Pass to enter, but he politely pointed to a door where I would be allowed to step into the Administration Building. So I entered the Door and noted I was in a small Coridore with several chairs (which were un-upholstered for discomfort, in order to discourage Aplickants from sticking around the Studio any longer than possible). And behind a small Grill a very pleasant Lady was being aproached by a nice looking Young Girl who said she wanted to see somebody about getting into the Movies. But the Lady behind the Grill Work said,

"I'm sorry, dear, but there isn't going to be any casting today."

So then the Girl started to leave in dissapointmint, and I was just going to follow her when the Lady behind the Grill Work said,

"Hay there! Miss! Come back here, will you?"

So I thought she wanted to call the Other Girl back and I oblidgingly said,

"I'll go get her for you."

But the Grill Work Lady said,

"I didn't mean her, dear. I meant you."

So I stepped up to the Grill, and the Lady asked who I wanted to see. So I told her I didn't know anybody, but I would like to get in the Movies, and enquired if she could please tell me when they would be casting.

So she looked me over for quite a few moments and finally said,

"And you don't know anybody, dear?"

So I said,

"No."

So then she appeared incredulis and said,

"How long have you been in Hollywood?"

So I said,

"Since day before yesterday."

And she said,

"But where were you all day yesterday?"

So I said,

"I was sleeping."

So she said,

"I thought you said you didn't know anybody."

So then I had to start in and explane everything that had happened to me since I arrived.

So then she said that I had better set down and let her line up an interview for me or else she might lose her job.

So she called somebody up on the phone, named Mr. Harris. But his Secretary said he was in Conference at the momint. So then the Lady asked if I would like to read a Magazine while I was waiting, and she gave me the *Hollywood Reporter* (which was going to be Mommy's daily reading matter from that day on). And I read the Gossip Collom for the first time, but I little knew my own name was going to be mentioned in it the very next morning, and that later on I was seldim going to ever be emitted from that Collom.

Well, as I set there reading, fresh Aplickants kept coming in, and getting themselves dismissed. But they paid me very little attention, because Aplickants had their mind on their own Career. But pretty soon I began to hear a loud rumpus, of one man calling another man names. So the Grill Work Lady spoke up and said,

"That's Mr. Harris, dear, so you won't have to wait much longer."

But I couldn't help feeling divident over the harsh landguage Mr. Harris had a command of. For by this time his voice was getting very close and I could hear him plainly say,

"If you, or any other Crook in Your G—— D—— Agency, ever sets foot in this Studio again, I'll fire every Policeman on the Lot."

And then there merged through the Door the very first man who was ever destinated to be your Mommy's Husband. For it was the popular Agent, Bert Griggsby (who is so well-built he could of easily became a Leading Man, except he hates work). And while Bert was stepping into the Coridore, he was dusting his coat off, so it looked as if Mr. Harris must of given him a shove against one of the antiqued Spanish Walls. But he very chipperly said to the Grill Work Lady,

"Well, Veronica, the Master Mind has just kissed me off!"

But as she started evincing her sympathy for him, Bert suddenly noted Mommy. So he politely sauntered away from Veronica and said,

This poster was drawn by some artist who never even had an interoduction to Mommy, and which I never, by no means, would ever of posed for.

"And whom might you be, Little Lady?"

But before Mommy could answer, Veronica spoke up and said, very strickly,

"Leave her alone, Bert. She's here to see Mr. Harris."

But paying her no attention, he said,

"Who manages you, honey?"

So I told him,

"Nobody."

Well, the next thing Mommy knew, I was being pushed ahead of Bert into Mr. Harris'es Office as a cammaflage to get him back in there. And Bert's psychology was very good, because the momint he said he represented Mommy, Mr. Harris stated we could both set down.

So then I set there in a daze and lissened to them dicker over me. And it turned out that Mr. Harris had been in a quarandary for a long time, trying to cast the roll of a girl who was supposed to lure men to their distruckshun. So Bert started warning him that the Studio had better get somebody, like me, who could startle the Publick into believing a script that was pretty feeble.

Well, after their haggel had gone on for a long while, Bert finally agreed to sign Mommy to a Seven-Year-Term with Mr. Harris that was to be continjint on my Screen Test the next day being successful.

Well, Bert escorted me out of Mr. Harris'es office in a daze. And then he took me to luncheon at Romanoffs fabilis restaurant. And as we were being politely escorted to Bert Griggsby's Private Booth, he told Mommy I had ruined every other Agent's lunch at Romanoffs that day, because he had been the first one to spot me.

And so Mommy set there and gazed around at a whole bevy of Film Stars in the Flesh, who, I could note, were gazing at me in the Flesh also. For I was learning that any Girl who got herself escorted by Bert Griggsby very quickly got in the Lime Light. Because Bert made a specialty of discovering Girls and it was a point of pride with him that they seldim failed to click.

But during luncheon it was very bewildering to lissen to Bert's large fund of technickal vernackuler and his ability to "ad-lib" comedy dialogue. And I am sure he would of felt dissapointed in Mommy, if I hadn't of been able to mention the Race Track back in Kansas, and also to call a few prominint Horses by name, which made it sound as if I had a great many more experiences in Life than I had actually had. And Mommy was also aided by my personal apearance, which always caused people's opinion of me to augmint beyond anything that had happened to me yet. So that day Bert never found out my knowledge of the Tracks consisted cheefly in pulling the bastings out of the Jockey's Silks who rode at them.

But the thing which mostly empressed Bert was when I was able to finally drag in the name of Mr. Pendergast. Because the meer Racket of being a Movie Agent became pale in comparison with Mr. Pendergast's whole Empire of Important State-Wide Graft. And when I finally found an opening to state that Mr. Pendergast used to buy Champagne for Mommy, back in old K.C., Bert was actually bowled over.

Well, to this day Mommy can't remember if I ate any luncheon, or even what I ordered (although it must of been something-or-other that was Alla Mode). But

I was sure that the luncheon had turned out a success, because the momint it was over, Bert said he was going to go and play a Round of Golf, so he could start Mommy's Publicity Campaign in the Men's Locker Room at Hillcrest. So he escorted me back to the Hotel and said he would take me to dine early at the Mocambo, so I could get back for a good night's sleep before my Screen Test. And when we parted, Bert admonished me to stay strickly in my own room, and rest.

But resting was out of the question. So all afternoon Mommy set and looked out the window, feeling highly anxious about my Test, and watching the traffick role by, and wondering if the time would ever come when I would own a Roadster.

Well, that night Bert took Mommy to the Mocambo, and it was more glamrous than even Romanoffs. For although the men, as usual, were meerly in their Golf-Togs, the famous Girl Stars were dressed up in their most gorgeous Formals and wearing their Mink Wraps that were of every other shade except the shade of Minks.

Well, that night Bert wouldn't allow anybody else to dance with Mommy (which went so far as to even exclude Bela Lugosi). But on the way back to the Hotel it was fairly easy to hold Bert off, because the momint he saw that I commanded his respeck, he desisted. For Bert had an ardint interest in not wanting to upset Mommy and ruin my Screen Test.

But all night long I layed awake and worried about it, so by the next morning I was shaking with nerves. But to my surprize, when I went to look in the glass, I looked my best. And when Bert called for me he told

Mommy to not worry, for he had been in communication with Mr. Harris and arranged a Test with a minnimum amount of acting to it. For it seems they had both agreed that in Mommy's case emotion didn't need to be too obligitery.

Well, at the Standard Studio they issued Mommy into the Make-Up Departmint, where the Union Operators did my hair and put a Pan-Chromatic Make Up on me. And then, in a daze, I went through the highly technickal details of a Test. But the acting didn't turn out so well, because the next day Mr. Harris called Bert into his office and withdrew Mommy's Seven-Year-Offer. But he said he would let me stay at Standard as an Extra, on a week-to-week basis, for $75 a week. And Bert had seen my Test himself, so he agreed.

Well, in Hollywood good-looking new girls keep arriving on every Train and Bus and Aeroplane. And one day Paulette Goddard got to town, so all we other new arrivals lost our novelty. And Mommy felt very guilty over making Bert Griggsby waste all his time on me those first few hours. For the only thing he got out of it was a meer 10%, which only mounted up to Seven Dollars and Fifty Cents, on the weeks I was able to get work. And when a Girl can't earn money enough to be worth all her Agent's trouble, there's naturally only one thing of value she can give him, which is her Time. So I had to give Bert much more of it than Mommy would otherwise of done.

So the next Year and a Half turned out to be one continuous Tumoil. And I would of given anything if Bert had wanted to marry Mommy at that period, instead of later on. (Although, to give Bert credit, he always used to say there was nothing he would drather do in the whole, wide World than to want to get married.)

Well, Mommy anyhow went to work at Standard, on

a Week-to-Week Basis. But I soon realized my Salary wasn't going to pay the bill at the Beverly Wilshire, and Taxi Fare back-and-fourth-every-day to Culver City. So I took the advise of some of the other Contrack Girls and moved into the Cal-U-Met Hotel acrost the Tracks from the Studio.

Well, the acting required of Mommy at Standard was a combanation of setting down in front of the Camera all day or else standing up. But my cheef job was to pose in Stills for the Advertising Departmint, wearing Shorts or a Bathing Suit, or lightly draped to solemize some Holiday. But we girls would have to pose for Christmas shots in August, dressed in a hot fur Bathing Suit, or else they'd shoot us during the rainy season, wearing a pair of chilly Rompers, to comimerate Fathers Day.

And Bert had enformed Mommy that a Girl with a Week-to-Week Deal at Standard had to be constintly on the Key Vive to keep from getting dropped. So after a hard day's work there were always countless invitations to except, such as being pleasant to the Executive Groop, or else substituting for the verious Stars, on dates. For there was a constint Influx of Visiting Exhibiters from the East who wanted to go back Home and claim they had taken some promanint Name to some Night Club. And I am sure those Exhibiters behaved with empiccible Galantary towards the Girls at Home. But after all, they were in Hollywood, on a rush visit, and they couldn't take the time.

Only there was one Escort Mommy never minded going out with. For Mr. Monroe was an elderly, rotund type who held the job of Cheef Canvas Stitcher in the

Scenic Department, and he didn't pay any more attention to a girl's aluremint than as if I was Martha Ray. But he was unordinately proud of a Hobby he had developed, of going to the Owl Drug Store and ordering the Soda Clerk to mix several verious diferent kinds of Soup (which he would carefully select) into a Bowl, and then call it a "Soup Cocktail." So sometimes it was amuseing for Mommy to except his invitation, and sit on a stool at the Lunch Counter, and make him concockt more and more peculiar combanations. But on the other hand, I had to eat them. So Mr. Monroe and his "Soup Cocktails" could turn out to frequintly be boresome.

And anyhow, I wanted to desperately stay Home and improve myself, and study for my Career (which took a great deal of concentration because of Mommy's previous lack of scholarship). So the most renumerative evenings I ever spent were when I used to be able to dash away from the Studio, and rush to the Drug Store, and eat my Hamburger and Pie Alla Mode, and then hurry up stairs, alone, and dwelve into my Numerolidgy.

Well, at the Cal-U-Met Hotel one of the most adorible inmates was Lalla Bates, whom in those days was just as far from being a Famous Star as Mommy was. And a Firm Friendship grew up betwixt Lalla and I (and we would of gone on being the best of Chums if we hadn't of finally bought Estates in diferent Districks).

But in one respeck the Temperamints of Lalla and I were completely opasite to one another. For, to Lalla, any person of the Male Gender was so stimulating that she was more than eager to meet them half way, and her Motto seemed to be "The More the Merrier." So Mommy used to jokeingly bet Lalla that she could even go out with Mr. Monroe and not be able to keep her mind on his soup cocktails.

And as if spending her Time on the men was not enough, Lalla also loved to spend her money. So she would be constintly buying a new Slide Trombine for some Member of some Band, or else a pair of Emported British Riding Britches for some Assistint Director to wear on the Set. And if she'd ever of fallen in love with a Ditch Digger, Lalla would of wanted to buy him the Panama Canal.

But Mommy preferred to do my Day-Dreaming all alone, sitting in some Movie Theatre, with my Pop Corn, and gazing at Walter Pigeon or Clyde Babcock on the Screen (just like I did back in Kansas City). And when I was forced to be with Escorts, I finally worked out a plan of meerly considering it in the catta-gory of "Office Hours."

But after a year and a half, the opertunity came, at last, for Mommy to step on the first Ring of the Ladder to Stardom. For a few blocks down the Boulevard from the Cal-U-Met Hotel was the Pinnacle Picture Cor-poration, where pictures of the "Quicky" Type were shot, on an extreemly limited budgit.

But Pinnacle Pictures could never afford Big Names, so they had to make sure that the Subjeck Matter was

In Hollywood there is an old addige that every Star has had her bubble bath.

absorbant. And the Proprietor, Danny Todd, had developed a Policy of shooting Scripts that had a strong tendincy towards breaking the Censureship Regulations.

Well, Danny Todd had "cleaned-up" on a picture which deplored the Unplanned Parenthood which Pinnacle claimed was privilent in High Schools. And Danny liked to make sure that every new production would excell all his past acheevements, so after wracking his brains for weeks, he got the idear of shooting a Documintery which would deal with the subjeck of Nudism. But Danny realized that even more important than the Subject-Matter, was to find some Girl who could portray the Heroin and live up to the Publick's expectations. So one day when Mommy was out on Washington Boulevard looking for the Good-Humor-Man, Danny interoduced himself and, out of the Blue, cast me for the Starring Roll.

And while I stood there, unable even to gasp the import of what Danny was saying, he went right on, useing the type of "Double Talk" for which he is famous for, and without mentioning the Subjeck of his Script, he said it would make my everlasting Reputation.

Well, I told Danny to get Bert Griggsby on the phone and repeat his offer to star me. And Mommy was so thrilled I forgot all about a Good Humor, and went straight Home to my Room, and waited for the phone to ring. For I was sure Bert would soon be calling up, to tender his congratulations. So when the phone finally rang, Mommy started to shake so hard I fumbled the receever.

But it wasn't Bert. For it was Danny calling up to say

that Bert had just flew to New York. So Danny asked me to come right over to Pinnacle, so he and I could personally work the arrangemints out to his satisfaction.

Well, I rushed right over, and Danny told me the roll would pay a hundred and twenty-five dollars a week, with a Three Weeks Guaranty, and that I wouldn't need to supply any wardrobe. But when Mommy asked how soon I could have the Script and begin to study my roll, Danny said he would have to tell me the plot verbally because he had only worked it out that morning while shaving and hadn't had the time to jot it down yet . . . "on asbestis."

Well, Mommy didn't like the sound of Danny's phrase "asbestis," but he told me to not worry, because I would soon see that there was a great deal of uplift to it. So then Danny called in his Script Writer, Mr. Bruce, who turned out to be a man of great distinction, but, to Mommy's surprize, Colored. For Mr. Bruce was the Add Writer for the *Central Avenue Press,* who condiscendid to work on Scripts for Pinnacle in his spare time. But before telling his plot, Danny said he wanted to get the "Mass Reaction" to it, so he was going to assimble his whole Studio Force. So he called in the Office Boy, and the three of us set there and reacted, while Danny paced back and fourth and began to outline his Plot.

And then Danny told how Mommy was going to portray a Girl Reporter who was sent by a Yellow Type of Journal to cover a Nudist Camp and expose it as being sensational. But the Heroin (whose name would be Miss Kent) would arrive there in the Spirit of sarcasm

129

and, while looking the Nudists over, be always ready to wise-crack about everything (which would supply the comedy elimint).

But then, one day, Miss Kent would get in conversation with one of the Better-Built Nudists, who would make her realize she had been in the wrong. So when Oveta Kent preceeded to write her artickle, she would take the opasite Angle from the one her paper suggested and lose her job. But by that time she wouldn't mind dismissal because she had Nudism to fall back on.

Well, Mommy spoke up with a sinking heart to ask whether the Sceenes of Miss Kent, after she got converted, would be Long-Shots? Or if I could count on them being merely Close-Ups of my Facial Reper-cushions? For I had begun to greatly fear the picture was not going to trumpt up any respeck for me in Bert Griggsby.

But Danny promised on his word of Honor that the only Shot of Miss Kent after her conversion would be the Final Fade-Out, where she walked up the Open Road, towards the Main Entrants of the Nudist Camp, in the Sunset, wearing her Taylor Maid, and meerly beginning to reverintly take her jacket off as she pre-ceeded.

Well, when Danny asked for the Mass Reaction to his Plot, the Office Boy spoke up and said he thought the mildness of my Final Fade-Out lacked Danny's usual Sense of Showmanship and would cause audiences to feel frusterated. But Danny said that a more satisfying finish would only cause Police interferince, so he planned to crowd all his Showmanship into the Art Work on the Advertisemints.

And then Danny's Script Writer spoke up and said, "Mr. Todd, you are incorrigibil!" which made Danny puff all up with pride.

Well, to save expense, the Picture had to be a Documintery, with Amateur Actors (except for Mommy and the Male Lead). And to save building any Sets, it was going to be mainly shot in the Nudist Camp at Elsanore, which gladly gave their permission, because of the opertunity to explane the Dignity of Nudism to the general Publick.

And Pinnacle Productions, besides being non-Censure Proof, were also non-Union, so the working hours were not mentioned in Mommy's Contrack. (But they worked out to ultimately be 18 hours a day.)

But the worse shock of all was when the Company (encluding Danny, and the Director, and the Camera Crew, and the Male Lead and Mommy) pulled up to the Main Gate and it turned out that nobody would be allowed to enter if garbed. For the Outside Gatekeeper (who was required by the Highway Patrol to wear a Pair of Shorts) said it was the only way we could show the sincerity of our Belief in Nudism.

Well, Mommy became so dispondint I told Danny I would drather give up my roll than take my garmints off. But Danny reminded me of the old Addidge that "The Show Must Go On." And the whole Company promised they would look the other way, and give Mommy 15 minutes Head-Start, so I could quickly dash through the Camp and get into my Costume (which required me to wear the Taylor Maid suit of a Girl Reporter). And Danny reminded me that the only persons who would look Mommy's way were the Nudists themselves, who would be in the same predicamint I was in, and unable to commint.

Well, if Mommy had quit and walked off the picture, it would of taken Danny the whole morning to dash over to Washington Boulevard and pick up a new Star. And then the Male Lead begged me to not upset the Shooting Schedule, because he had to get back home before his wife had a baby. And anyhow it was hot.

But never in my Life has Mommy created the small amount of attention I receeved while sideling along the pathway of that Camp. For I was soon to learn that Nudists are a type of personality which is only intrigeed in exhibiting their own selves, and they take no interest what-so-ever in the personalities of anybody else.

So by the time I reached the clump of tents which our Company were going to occupy, I was not nearly so ashamed of myself as I was of those Nudists. For their Age-Groop was mainly beyond the Forties, and they were the least-well-built-body of persons of both Genders that Mommy has ever had to observe. (While their physical detrimints were only exceeded by the shocking amount of respecktibility they would of had if they had any clothes on.) So Mommy felt very much releeved to even get into my hot Taylor Maid. And when I came out of my Tent and had to incounter my friends among the Hollywood Contingint, I inveritably turned my gaze towards the tree tops, while the Camera Crew avoided Spectater-Imbarrassmint by shooting the Cast from behind verious rocks and clumps of bushes.

But Danny had a bad habit of egging those Nudists on, which to a whole Body of Exhibition Lovers drove them almost hysterical. And some of the Routines they developed could at best be only called "silly." For one of them was a Game they played, while replinishing the Water Tank in their Kitchen Tent, by forming a long Line of Nudists, and handing buckets of water from one to another, beginning at the Creek and ending at the Tent, and chanting the phrase "Buckety-Buckety" in unisen as they did it.

And the Leader of that Bucket Brigade was an elderly Male Nudist, who was in his glory. And, in the first few minits, he invented methods of "Hogging the Camera" that Mommy hadn't been able to avolve in months (and which, from that time on, I copied to advantage).

But one very bad elimint of the whole proceedure was the Dining Tent, which was very hot to begin with, and had a strong tang of gasoline fumes from the stove which perminated the whole atmosphere. And then those Nudists had an un-apetizing habit of attaching Paper Napkins to the skin with their Chewing Gum. So in those three weeks Mommy lost seven pounds, through loss of apetite while having to contimplate Nudism at the dining table.

And there was also the greatest dificulty for the Male Lead and I to get any "mood" into our love Scenes. Because looking at Nudists makes the whole subjeck of Romance out of the question. And the assignmint turned out to only have one compinsation. Because sometimes when the heat would become absolutely unbearable, I would slip out of my Taylor Maid. For by that time even the Hollywood contingint was too fed up with Nudism to pay Mommy any attention.

CHAPTER 12

Well, after Danny's Film was shot, I had to go back to doing Extra Work at Standard, because I wouldn't be a Star until the Picture got released. But I used to lay awake night after night, and worry what was going to happen to me next. Because one time, just before Bert went to New York, he had condiscindid to take me to a Night Club, and left me alone there, crying. So a Stranger had stepped up and patted Mommy on my shoulder and called me a "Poor little tramp," which made me suddenly realize it was the first kind word I'd had in a long while.

So I had developed a veritable obsession to make Bert want to get married. And Mommy's Conscience got in a State where I used to invert my gaze every time I had to pass the small Baptist Church on my way to the Studio. For back in Kansas I had gone to Baptist Sunday School.

Well, Bert ultimately got back from New York, but when he heard about Mommy's engagemint with Pinnacle, he went into a Fuhrer and said not to depend on him, in the future, to proteck my interests, because I had ruined my Reputation working for Danny's outfit, which was so ill-legal I could of held out for three hundred and fifty dollars a week. So he walked out of the Dressing Room at Standard and slammed the door.

Well, sitting there in a daze, I decided I had only myself to blame. For as time went on, and Bert's behavior had got worse and worse, I ought to of considered that the dept of gratitude I owed him was cancelled, and refrained from seeing him any more. Only by being with him I at least knew he wasn't with some other Girl, who might get him in a Spot where he would have to marry *her*.

But that day while Bert had been telling Mommy he was through, he was over-heard by a Star of Western Productions, named Jerry Jones, who happened to be parked acrost the Boulevard. And Jerry had always been wild to get Mommy to go out with him. But going out with Actors was not obligitery, so I politely got out of it by saying I was oficially going with Bert. But when Jerry heard Bert's final statemint, he began begging for dates again.

Well, Jerry had always showed me respeck, so I went out with him a few times, very formally. And then one night at the Trocadero, Jerry Jones accorded Mommy the first proposition of Marriage I had ever got, out of all the Escorts I had ever had.

Well, Jerry's dialogue had been a little bit overly-crude, but it was a real proposal, that would legalize Mommy's unmarried Statis. So I thanked him from the bottom of my Heart, and greatfully excepted.

But all that night I layed awake, and had to pinch myself to realize I wasn't dreaming. For Jerry was a

Star, even if his Pictures were of the "B" cattagory. And when sober, he was inveritably opolagetic of his previous behavior. But most of all, it would give me a chance, every time I encountered Bert Griggsby, to remind him that somebody had asked to marry me.

But just as I was dozeing off that morning, the phone rang. And it was Jerry, saying he had a feeling he had insulted me the previous evening. For he feared that while intoxicated, he had repeated a few "quotes" from his new Script which Mommy might construw into a proposal. So would I please forgive him and forget it?

Well, I naturally had to except Jerry's opolagy. But I hung up, and for quite a while I became despondint. And then finally I braced up and decided to try and find a substitoot for Numerolidgy, which had worked out with such bad results in my case. So that evening, when I went over to the Owl Drug Store to get my dinner (very thankfully) alone, they were having a Special Sale, on Baked Sea Bass, Kleenex and Text Books in Astrology. So I purchased the 3-way combanation and began my Study of the Stars.

And then one evening, not long afterwards, I found out that my "Cusp of Venis" indicated the next day might bring Mommy a "Rewarding Experience." So, in the morning, I hurried over to the Studio on the Key Vive.

Well, when Mommy went on the Set, garbed for a Napoleonic Ball in the days of the Umpire, the Head of the Standard Studios, Mr. Harris, himself, stepped up and stopped me. And the very Stoppage was, itself, a "Rewarding Experience." Because, after Mr. Harris saw my Film Test, he had very seldim even nodded at me. For to Mr. Harris, Sex Apeal is always synomious to success. And his emotions over a Girl never come to Life until after she gets famous.

So Mr. Harris told Mommy he wanted me, and Lalla, and two of the other Girls, to dine at the Mocambo that night, with a Groop of Imported South-American Exhibiters, who were of such financial distinction that Mr. Harris, himself, would accompany the party. So he said for Mommy to immediately get a Requisition for an evening gown, and tell the Wardrobe Mistress to pick one out that was as spareing in the use of material as possabil.

Well, the gown they gave me was even more scanty than the one I wore on the Napoleonic Set, so I felt I was looking my best when I entered the Mocambo with Mr. Harris'es party. And as we set down, I looked acrost and noted Bert at another table, accompanied by a Strange Man who he had personally conducted back from New York with him, plus the two most eminent Stars belonging to Bert's Agency (who were fairly overpowered with Jewellry).

Well, the Strange Man in Bert's party was no mystry to any Reader of the *Hollywood Reporter*. For Bert had decided to break into the "Production End" of Pictures, by forming Packadges (which encluded a Best Seller, plus a Star, plus a Script Writer, plus a Director)

 In your Mommy's conception of Mary-the-Queen-of-the-Scotts, the Director shot eight reels of Mommy feeling sorry for myself.

and then selling the whole Packadge to some Major Studio. But to buy a Best Seller required Cash, which required a Backer. So this one's name was "Mr. Douglas Frizzell," and the Gossip Collom of the *Reporter* had been "kidding" every move Bert made with him, from the momint he had first gone back East to find somebody of Mr. Frizzell's type.

Well, that night when Bert's Backer looked acrost that room and spotted Mommy, something electrical seemed to happen to him. And the momint Mommy started dancing past Bert's table with the South American allotted to me, Mr. Frizzell would rise clear up out of his chair, in the hope of some indication from Mommy to cut in. But I would never of dreamed of deserting my South American because I thought Mr. Harris would be enfuriated.

But when we went back to our table, Mr. Harris told me to go ahead and do it. Because he had wanted to get even with Bert for worming his way back into Standard that day, by hiding behind Mommy's skirts and making him think I had ability. So Mr. Harris turned my South American over to Lalla (who was capable of handling the whole contingint), and then he said that he, himself, would dance past Bert's table with me and for me to incouradge Mr. Frizzell to cut in.

Well, Mommy has never had an easier assignmint, for one trip past Mr. Frizzell turned the trick. And when we had finished dancing and Mr. Frizzell escorted me back to my table, Mr. Harris envited him to stay and have a drink. So Mr. Frizzell fairly leaped at the oppertunity, and set there, under the glowering eyes of Bert, while Mr. Harris encouradged him to wamble on, and on, telling everybody at the table how much I re-simbled both his Wife and his Daughter, back in Ohio, who's Snap Shots he took out of his wallit. (And that is the only time Mommy has ever been acused of re-simbling persons with infinitissimal eyes and the absints of a chin.)

Well, then Mr. Frizzell told Mr. Harris how his Daughter had got married and left Home, and his Wife spent all her time learning Yogi, so he was free to go into the Picture Industry and put his idears to work which, before retiremint, he had regulated to the mani-facture of poreous undergarmints.

So Mr. Harris started drawing Mr. Frizzell out on the subjeck of his idears. And Mr. Frizzell said it was his contintion that so many pictures were being made fee-turing Catholicism (with Stars garbed like Priests or Nuns) that he felt something had ought to be done along the same lines for the Baptists. And Mr. Frizzell felt that Mommy was just the type of an upstanding girl who could portray the Lead, and lose nothing by getting wet in a Tank. And when I told Mr. Frizzell that I was brought up to be a Baptist, it clinched the matter, right there at the table, and he said if Mr. Har-ris would make the Film, he would finance it.

Well, Mr. Harris had no need of any outside money (for those were the good old days Before Television, when no reputable Studio ever dreamed the day would come when they would ever need financing). But to make sure that Bert would never get Mr. Frizzell back again, Mr. Harris envited him to come over to Standard the next day, and out-line his Thoughts to the Scenario Departmint. And then he told Mr. Frizzell to hang onto his money.

Well, nothing touches the Heart of any Backer so much as being told that his idears are feesible, and he can hang onto his money. For in their subconscious mind, there always lurks the distasteful term of "Sucker." So from that momint on, wild horses couldn't of dragged Mr. Frizzell back to Bert's table. And before midnight, we watched Bert steer his two eminent Stars out of the Mocambo, in a huff.

Well, at 4 A.M., Mr. Frizzell courtiously escorted me back to the Cal-U-Met, and shook hands with Mommy gallantly at the doorway. But as I stepped into the empty Lobby, I suddenly saw Bert sitting there. And as Mommy stood stockstill, looking at him, Bert rose up, with a consumate smile on his face. And, full of assurince that he could use Mommy as his contack to get Mr. Frizzell back, he spoke as though he had never imployed anything but Pet-Names on me in his whole Life and said,

"Hello, Delicious!"

And then something inside of Mommy must of snapped. For all-of-a-sudden, I heard myself calling Bert names I'd been storeing up mentally for a whole year and a half.

Well, as I went on, Mommy's vocabulery gained momintim. And as I became more and more un-lady-like, a note of new-born admiration started creeping into Bert's countenince.

And then, right out in that open Lobby, Bert started to evince a recurrince of interest in me, that was stronger than any he had ever shown in our whole relationship. So I suddenly realized that I had had to become vulger in order to bring out Bert's tenderness. But when I finally called him the most truthful sinomym I could think up, and ordered him to leave that Lobby, the Truth finally got under Bert's skin, and he sauntered out, while Mommy dashed upstairs and, for the first time in months, slept just like a Baby. Because useing a fowl vocabulery had clarified the atmosphere, and put a respeckful end to a humiliating association.

Well, the next morning I woke up in the same vindicative spirit, and from that time on, I deeviously kept Mr. Frizzell in custody, evening after evening. And in the day-time, when I was busy working, Mr. Harris had given orders for one of the Junior Writers (who was at the Studio to learn Script Writing on a Scholarship) to constintly keep Mr. Frizzell company and to even jot down his idears in Continuity Form (for practise).

But Mr. Frizzell spent most of his time on the Sound Stages, getting aquainted with Mommy's Acting Methids. And the whole Company was enjoying the joke so heartily that our Director, Buzz O'Connor, used to sometimes trump up a Sceen for me to do (from a tragic Plot, intitled *The Letter* by Somerset Mawm) that had no connection with the Script we were actually shooting. And Buzz would order the Camera Man to shoot Mommy, without putting any Film in the Camera. So I would cheerfully go along with their "gag" and give Mr. Frizzell the thrill of his Life. For in his opinion, I could do no wrong.

Well, every time Mommy would return to the Cal-U-Met, there would be reams of telephone slips, asking me to "Please call up my Agent." For Bert was becoming more and more frantick, and the Collomist on the

Reporter was taking a very subtil means of "kidding" him, by printing daily reports of Mr. Frizzell's activities with me. (And it was those squibbs in the *Reporter* which institooted Mommy's first daily apearince in Print.)

But one evening, when Mr. Frizzell was safely tucked away in his hotel suite with the flu, Mommy found time to spend on my Astrolidgy and I learned that Saturn was going into a terrible Aspick to my Sign of Bearth (which indicated that a period of Sabatical tribulations was at hand).

Well, the first evening Mr. Frizzell was able to be up-and-around, Mommy's adverse Aspick worsened. For when he came to get me, for dinner, his face was taut. And instead of wanting to flount Mommy around the Mocambo or Romanoffs (where they were always shooting Snap Shots of us) he escorted me to the private retreet that was institooted by the late Thelma Todd, called La Joya. And we were no sooner seated in a secludid booth than Mr. Frizzell took a newspaper from his overcoat pocket and opened it with quivering hands, and showed Mommy an Announcemint of my forthcoming Pinnacle Production (which Danny had unfortunately titled *The Nude Deal,* in honor of Our President of the Period).

Well, as Mommy set there, looking at it, I couldn't say a word. For the Art-Work on that Ad was a picture of my face, combined with a delineation of Mommy's physique which had been drawn by hand. But the Artist had compleetly omitted the Taylor Maid Suit that had been a requisint of the Shooting Script.

And then Mr. Frizzell said all he wanted to know

144

was how any sweet girl like Mommy could of done it? So I bursted into tears, for I knew Mr. Frizzell was right. And it made me begin to feel that maybe Hollywood was hardening Mommy.

Well, when I was able to finally speak, I told Mr. Frizzell how totally garbed I had been in the Film (even to the extint of my Taylor Maid being a little bit mannish). But after I was able to make him understand, Mr. Frizzell told Mommy that his situation was "a pretty complicated one." For he said his Yogi Wife had been compleetly in accord with anything he wanted to do in Hollywood, so long as it left her alone with her Swami, and had Uplift. But he said Mrs. Frizzell would think it was "Mighty queer" of him to feature a Star in a Baptist Film Project who would be previously advertised, all over the country, advocating Nudism.

And Mr. Frizzell told Mommy that, even as things stood, he had been photographed with me far too frequintly, going places. So he said he would have to hurry Home, and make Piece with his Yogi Wife, before the bomb bursted.

So then Mr. Frizzell told Mommy he had found something out about my acting that he thought I ought to know. And, to my astroundmint, he said that one day while they were getting ready to shoot me in a big dramatic momint, he had found out there wasn't any film in the camera.

So Mr. Frizzell said that the next time they shot me acting, he had bribed the Camera Man to put some Film in. And the following day, when they ran the Rushes, he sneaked into the Projection Room, in the dark, to see the repercushions of my talent on the spectaters. And Mr. Frizzell said he felt it was only fair to let Mommy know that, when everybody in the room had ought to of been crying, they all roared with laughter. So Mr. Frizzell said he wanted to warn me that when my Director incouradged me to act, it was only because he had nefarious intentions.

And then Mr. Frizzell said he wanted me to give up the Films, and go to Switzerland, to a lovely Girls School, high up in the Alps, where no Pinnacle Production could ever perminate, and I could get prepared for a normal life of some kind. And he handed Mommy a large check, for a starter. But I told him it was a little bit too late for me to begin learning Swiss, and I had better stick to my career, But I promised Mr. Frizzell I'd take some lessons in acting, and watch my step with that Director. So that was the way things were left, when we finally seperated in front of the Cal-U-Met.

Well, the next morning, the whole of Los Angeles knew Mommy's face, from Pinnacle's advance announcemint. But Mr. Frizzell wanted Mommy to see him to the Train so desperately that I proteckted him by wearing dark goggles and covering my hair up, and we took our last drive down to the Station together. And I was happy to pervide Mr. Frizzell with that one big momint, in his whole life, of secret stealth.

But when the Train was ready to start, and we shook hands, and said, "Good-bye," there were tears in the eyes of us both. For I felt pretty depressed to be parting from such a lovely old gentleman who had always treated me respeckful. (For poor Mr. Frizzell was so unsophisticated he's probably never realized, to this day, that his intentions had a single thing to do with Sex.)

Well, that morning, after the Train departed, Mommy was just starting to get into Mr. Frizzell's Hired Limousine, when I suddenly noticed a familiar figure dashing out of a familiar car. And, as I looked closer, I saw it was Bert who I could hardly recognize because of his hectical aspeck. For his face was white and it even lacked Bert's regular, meticilis, everyday shave. So I naturally thought he was there to blame Mommy over the final loss of Mr. Frizzell. But I was too emotionally upset over looseing Mr. Frizzell myself, to undergo a vialent Sceen with any Agent. So without giving Bert time to even open his mouth, I told him there was nothing he, or anybody else could do, to get Mr. Frizzell back. But then Bert suddenly stopped Mommy cold by saying,

"The hell with the Sucker!"

And then, standing there, and trembeling in every limb, Bert asked if Mommy would marry him.

Well, it took Mommy a few momints to even believe my ears. But Bert looked so misrabel I had to finally realize that he meant every word he spoke. So I told Mr. Frizzell's Hired Chauffeur to go his own way, and then I allowed Bert to drive me Home to Culver City.

Well, I set there beside Bert and lissened, in a daze, while he told Mommy that looseing Mr. Frizzell had been mild, in comparison to the frusteration of looseing a girl who had the tremendis amount of Publicity I had been getting in *The Hollywood Reporter*. And then Bert admitted he never knew the depths of his love for Mommy until I started calling him violent names and then holding out on him. So by the time we reached Culver City, your Mommy had condiscindid to become Mrs. Bertram Griggsby.

But the momint we reached the Cal-U-Met, I made Bert drop me. And then, in the hecticle state of releef and ecsticy I was in, I dashed breathlessly upstairs to my room, and put through a call to Jerry Jones. For Mommy had a feeling, at last, that I had learned the Nack of handeling the men. But I wanted to have one more test of it.

Well, Mommy's phone call reached Jerry at his Ranch House in Encino and I was even surprized at my own Self, for the harsh dialogue I was able to ad-lib, while upbraiding him for his neglect, since the time he had opolagized for proposing. And after Jerry had got over his first shock at Mommy's strong landguage, he very meekly said he'd dash right over from Encino, to opolagize in person.

So he got there in a jiffy. And then, setting in the Coffee Shoppe of the Cal-U-Met, as sober as a Judge, and meerly sipping Coca-Cola, Jerry Jones stammered out a proposal of Matrimony, to which he was careful to add that he wasn't quoting from any Script, but really meant it.

Well, Jerry's behavior clinched Mommy's Faith in myself and proved at last that Sex Apeal can be provocative of Marriage, if administrated vigerously, and then with-held. And Mommy knew that I need never be insulted again, for I could get married as much as I chose. So to serve Bert Griggsby right for everything he'd ever done to me, I promised Jerry I would marry him too.

CHAPTER 13

Well, Mommy became Mrs. Bertram Griggsby in a quiet wedding at the quaint old Mission Inn at Riverside. But we wanted everything to be very simple, so we only envited a small amount of intimate friends, and I asked Lalla Bates to be my Brides Maid. But the only acquaintince I had who was able to suggest a "Father" was Mommy's Friend in the Canvas Stitching Department. So I got the Studio to grant Mr. Monroe a half day off, to give me away, while Bert meerly had a couple of the Boys from the Agency for his Attendints.

And on our Wedding Day, Bert could hardly get over how cute it was of Mommy to ensist on driving him to Riverside myself, in the gorgeous, new Baby-Blue Cadilac Convertible he had given me for a Wedding Present (with a Course of Lessons how to drive it).

Well, our Marriage was solemnized by The Justice of the Piece, in the little Spanish Chapel of the Inn. And afterwards we attended a Champagne-Wedding-Breakfast in the historical old "Ramona Room," during which Mommy excused myself to powder my nose, and went out the back entrants, and jumped into the Groom's Wedding Gift, and gave him the slip. Because Mommy never intended to consomate that marriage. For all I wanted was to legalize the Past.

Well, Mommy drove straight out to Encino to announce to Jerry Jones that I had just got married to Bert impulsively but realized the mistake the momint I did it. But I ensisted on Jerry protecting my reputation by moving into the Beverly Wilshire Hotel for the duration of our Engagement. And then Mommy meerly went into hideing at his Ranch House.

But it became my first publicized Scandal. For the Publick never dwelved into Mommy's motovations, and started to falsely accuse me of being irratick. And when the Newspaper Reporters found Mommy and wanted an explanation of my course of action, I refused. For I've always remembered a Motto I learned from my little Jockey Dadda, who said to do anything to anybody I wanted to, but to never harm their means of making their living. And I felt if I publicized how Bert had treated me in our pre-numptial period, it might of hurt his professional integritty as an agent. While my professional integritty as a Star of Pinnacle Productions was (like Julious Cesar's Wife) beyond reproach.

But it anyhow gave Bert a wonderful oppertunity to sit in Night Spots, and talk to anybody who would lissen, and tell them how heartlessly I had ruined his

Faith in Womanhood. And he fairly revelled in the sympathy that everyone feels for a deserted Bride-Groom (especially Revellers of the Female Gender). So in about six weeks, Bert's attorneys were able to easily get our marriage annulled, by proving we never lived together after the Ceremony.

But then Mommy decided to not marry Jerry Jones, for I didn't really have anything serious against him. But when I tried to break the Engagemint, poor Jerry took to liquor with so much more facility than usual that Mommy begun feeling sorry for him. So I finally gave in to a simple Cowboy Ceremony at the Little Chapel of the Flowers in Forrest Lawn.

But getting married inside a Cimitery turned out, in Mommy's case, to be bad luck. For as soon as I became Mrs. Jones, Jerry made me give up my Career to meerly become the Lady of the House.

But being "Mrs. Jones" was pretty up-hill work. Because it required me to allow Jerry to be very rough, so that he could then become very opolagetic, and then grow very humbil. And I never decided which of Jerry's emotions were the most trying. For, when rough, he was noisy. And when opolagetic, he was repititious. And when humbil, boresome. And his only Saving Grace was that all his emotions were spuruous. For poor Jerry was an Actor.

Well, when Jerry had to be away from Home, working, he ensisted on me staying strickly in the confines of Encino and even hired Deteckatives to shadow Mommy. But I couldn't justly blame him, because my first marriage had given Mommy the reputation of a "Husband-Deserter."

But being bottled up in Encino caused lonesomeness to set in. For Mommy's friends were all at Culver City, too busy working, or looking for jobs, to pay visits during the day time. And in the evenings, Jerry stayed Home, which caused them all to do likewise.

Well, with nothing to do in Encino, Mommy started taking lessons in everything anybody ever thought of teaching along the San Fernando Boulevard (including Operatic Voice Culture, Snake Charming, Astral Contacks, Electrical Tatooing, and Trout Fishery).

But one day my Astral Professor said if Mommy didn't find some sort of a Psychic Outlet, I was in danger of permanintly looseing my Polarity. So Jerry promised he'd do something about it. But all he did was humiliate Mommy by dragging me to his Studio, and ensisting that they give me a contrack to play in his Westerns, where Jerry could be sure that he, himself, was making love to me. But Jerry's Film Corporation was run primarily for "The Kids," so they were able to make the excuse that my Pinnacle Production had erased Mommy from the Juvenile Field. And I was very releeved, because I didn't want my Career to be based on the fact of who I was married to.

But after about eight months something happened that made my Career start up again. For one night at a Stag Party, in Honor of a well known Producer's Birthday, they ran off some Film of the type seldom seen by the General Publick. For it consisted of "Blow-Ups,"

 The Studio decided to cheer the Publick up, so it had my authoress pen Bettina of the Big Top.

152

where Sceens are shot in which some un-for-seen mistake is made (such as when some wholesome Star, playing a Mother roll in some harmless Family Sceen, "blows up" in her lines, and bursts into epithets). And these Shots, if properly Cut and Titled, form an unconventional type of amusemint.

Well, the Shots they were showing that night had been collected by Jimmy McCoy, who had happened to cut the Sceen which I had performed for the benefit of Mr. Frizzell. So Jimmy thought it would be an amuseing edition to the evening's fun to put in a big Close-Up of Mommy.

Well, it turned out that one of the Guests at the Stag Party that night was the most artistic Producer in Hollywood, by which I mean, of course, Leo Montaigne. And Leo had bought a Best Seller titled *The Woman in Black,* which unfolded the Heart-rendering story of a good Man and his Wife, in the Middle West, who had been so faithful to each other that they even stayed away from the Country Club. But into the Life of that Husband there merged a Girl of such outstanding Sex Apeal that she broke their Marriage up and wrecked their Life.

Well, when Leo Montaigne produced a Picture, he was diferent from the rest of Hollywood. For he looked at everything from the viewpoint of Life, where the kind of Husbands who allow Sex Apeal to break up their Home, ought not to be treated like a Hero, but are in a position where it's more logical to "bounce gags" off them. So Mr. Montaigne had sent to New York for a Writer who had no reverince for unfaithful Husbands, and that Writer had dramatized the plot contrary to the usual Hollywood methid of treating Sex Apeal as a menice.

Well, on the morning after Leo Montaigne saw Mommy in that Shot, he went to the Business Head of his Studio, Mack Tumulty, and said he wanted Mommy for the roll of the Home Wrecker. But Mack was aghasted. For it was his opinion that to see a Girl like Mommy go after a Husband would cause every man in the audience to cringe, because the situation was bound to be universally close to Home. And Mack was furthermore afraid that falling for Mommy would make any Hero look like a Laughing Stock, to which Mr. Montaigne had meerly replied,

"Well . . . ?"

So Mack, being an inveterant Lady's Man, squirmed but he said if Leo ensisted, to go ahead. So they put a phone call through to Mommy, and told me to come right over to see Leo Montaigne.

Well, a call from Leo Montaigne was something many a Famous Star would hardly dare to dream of. So I jumped into my Wedding-Gift Cadilac and speeded right out of Encino (with a Deteckative close behind). And when I reached the Montaigne Lot, I was ushered into Leo Montaigne's private Bungaloo and set there, thrilled, while he made the arrangemints for my test next morning. And while driving back to Encino, in a daze, Mommy started to foamilate a Plan for my Future. For I knew that as soon as Jerry heard I was going to work with some other Leading Man, his reaction would ampily pervide the grounds for our Divorce.

But I soon found out I had something yet to learn about Actors. For Jerry, himself, had been trying to worm his way into Montaigne Productions for years, and he felt that Mommy might become an ideal Stepping Stone. So he readily agreed. (But in a way, I was glad to remane married, because I didn't want to burden the Montaigne Studios with a lot more adverse publicity at the very start.)

Well, the upshoot of the matter was that Mommy's Tests pleased Leo from every angle. But when it came to making out my Contrack, Jerry ensisted on a Clause which would allow him to Star with Mommy in the Production. So they went into a long haggle, with Leo staunchly proteckting his Studio. But when Jerry finally noted that Leo was ready to drop the whole idear of useing me, he suggested an alternite Clause which would allow him to borrow Mommy at some future date, to support him in a production at his own Studio. (For to have a Montaigne Star in his supporting cast would anyhow be a feather in Jerry's cap.) Well, Leo finally capitulated, so at last Mommy won the roll of that uproareous Siren.

Well, the release of *The Woman in Black* was historical. And over night, I bursted into Stardom. But at the same time, Jerry Jones made me cap my own Climax, with the most outstanding scandal of my whole career (to date).

chapter 14

Well, after Mommy's Hit in my first Montaigne Picture, Leo realized it was going to take a long while to prepare my next Vehickle along the meticilis lines he required, so he decided to loan Mommy out at once, and get it over with. And without even a chance to enjoy my Fame, I was whisked over to Western Productions, to play a roll in support of Jerry Jones.

But any Husband whos wife becomes promanint after marriage has only got one way to show his superiority which is to rise above it and sneer. So we had no sooner started shooting than Jerry's behavior became a mass of contridictshuns. For the Script required him to act very dividint towards the Character portrayed by Mommy, of the wealthy Ranch Owner's Neece. But the momint the Camera stopped grinding, Jerry's dividints turned to sarcasm, or even worse.

Well, one morning the Montaigne Press Departmint

delivered a Truck-Load of Fan Mail to Mommy, right out on the open Set, in full view of the whole Company, and the disgrace became more than Jerry could bear. So he accused me of luring Lester Cummings, our Camera man, into taking Close-Ups of me. And Jerry finally became so vialent I told him I was through with him, for good. And I would of greatfully moved back to my old room at the Cal-U-Met if our Company hadn't of been skeduled to leave for the Dessert that evening, on Location. But Mommy anyhow made our Manager get me a Drawing Room on a diferent part of the Train than Jerry, and I evaided running into him at the Station when Lester and I got on the Train.

Well, that night in the Lounge Car after dinner, Jerry started drinking with a Groop of Traveling Salesmen, who began to flatter him for being married to such a stimulating Wife. And they finally put Jerry in a mood where he felt incombrint to publically take advantage of being the Husband of the famous Effie Huntriss. So after loudly stating that it was "time to hit the hay," Jerry went to his own Compartmint, to get all dressed up, in the old fashioned type of a Night Shirt (with splits on the side) which he ensisted on wearing, both in and out of Films. Because in Jerry's mind pyjamas were not ruggid. And then he caused a Furer by wavvering through the Train in his Sleeping Garmint, remarking to all the occupints as he passed through,

"Good Night, Folks! Here I go, to my custimerry Rendyvoo with little Mrs. Jones."

Now, if Jerry had walked through a Train in the East, garbed in nothing but a short Night Shirt, he would of been apprehendid, and placed safely back in his own Compartmint for the Night. But Sleeping-Car Porters in the Hollywood Area have got so accustomed to Film Actors on Trips that scarcely anything startles them. So not a single Porter stopped Jerry as he neared Mommy's Drawing Room where I was setting absint-mindedly alone with Lester.

But at that period I had become so fed-up with the whole idear of Manhood, in any form, that I had en-sisted on Lester leaving the door wide open. So all Jerry needed was one quick peek to see that his vaunted Wife was alone in a Drawing Room with some other man.

Well, it put Jerry in a Spot, for if he attacked Lester, Lester could of hit below the belt by shooting adverse Stills of Jerry during the remainder of the Picture. And Jerry couldn't of hit me, because he had a ruleing to never strike a Girl in Publick. So when Lester placed his arm around Mommy for pretection, Jerry started to screech for the Porter to stop the Train, and let him get off, in the open Dessert, where the air was unpalooted.

Well, Lester sent the Porter (who was turning almost white in terrer) for our Company Manager, Herman Weiss. And while waiting for him, Jerry stood there, blameing Mommy at the top of his voice, and throwing the whole Car in a Tumoil. But the momint Jerry spotted Herman entering our Car, he began to shreek that he was going to jump off the Train and started running towards the Observation Platform.

So everyone ran after Jerry to stop him, and just as he was climbing over the Back Rail, Herman grabbed him around the waist and reminded Jerry that a leap off that moving Train might break his leg and hold the Picture up for weeks. And Herman pleaded,

"You wouldn't want to wreck the whole Production, would you, Pal?"

But Jerry reinterated,

"The Hell I wouldn't!"

At which, Jerry reached into his mouth and jerked out his upper Bridge-Work, and hearled it far off into the receeding Dessert.

Well, Pandymoniam bursted out. And when Herman dropped his grasp on Jerry, to pull the Bell Rope, to stop the Train, Jerry jerked out his lower Bridge-Work and hurtled it off the *opasite* side of the Platform, into a totally diferent portion of the Dessert.

Well, it seemed to take forever to stop that Train. And then Herman was forced to put several members of our Crew off, into the wide open Dessert, with a full Set of Outdoor Lighting Equipment to search for Jerry's widely seperated bridge work.

So after we got started again, sleep was out of the question, and we all gathered in the Lounge Car, to compare notes on everything. And our Assistint Director (who had once prospeckted on the Dessert for Gold) felt sure that the beams from our Spot Lights would cause Jerry's dentures to shimmer in the dark. So everybody was starting to settle down and feel hopeful, when someone discovered that Jerry, himself, was missing. Well, we combed that whole Train through for him, to no avale. And finally we had to conclude that he had manadged to get off the Train with the Search Party during the excitemint.

So that was just what Jerry did and he had manadged to avoid attention in the dark, so there was not a single Soul to retane him when he started wandering into the empty Dessert, without any other objective than to feel sorry for himself.

But the next morning, when the Dawn started coming up, the shock of learning he was feeling Sea Sick on a Dessert, brought Jerry to his senses and he realized what he had done. So from that momint on, his sole objective was to get to the Office of his Dentist in downtown Los Angeles.

Well, after wandering for a while, Jerry manadged to reach a Highway, and followed Sign Posts, to the outskirts of a Dessert Town, where he came to a Hacienda, and noted a Roadster out in front, with a key in it. So in desperation he got in, and started speeding towards L.A.

But Jerry had only gone a few miles when he suddenly noted the Car was nearly out of Gas. So he halted at the first Roadside Station and yelled for the Attendint to come out and fill his Tank up.

Only when that Attendint came out, and saw a strange looking person, without a shave, or Bridge Work, garbed in a Night Shirt that had been torn by wandering through cactis plants for hours, he mistook him for a Dessert Rat and demandid paymint in advance. So Jerry told the Attendint to mail him the bill, for he was Jerry Jones, the Foremost Star of Western Pictures, who could buy and sell all the gasoline in California.

But Jerry's speech, without his Dentures, sounded anything but Western. So that Attendint excused himself to step inside a momint, and quietly phoned the Sheriff, who had just receeved a report on the stolen Car that Jerry happened to be driving. So the Sheriff got there in a jiffy, and Jerry was thrown into Jail for Car Stealing, Indeecint Garmints, trying to Get Gas without Intention of Paymint, and Impersonating a Famous Movie Star.

Well, that afternoon, as Jerry set, dazed, in a Dessert cell, he began to hear a distant radio stating that Louella Parsons and Hedda Hopper and the Associated Press were combing the whole country for Jerry Jones, the ruggid Star of Western Films who had romantickally dissapeared. (For Herman had been forced to naturally surpress the more undignified aspecks of Jerry's dissapearince.)

Well, the Nation-Wide Publicity would of warmed Jerry's Heart, if he had only had his Bridge-Work in. But all he could do was to set there and cower, for fear he would be found, and photographed, and that his Sound Track, without any Dentures, might indicate he wasn't even very masculine.

So several terribil days went by. But finally, when he was almost out of his mind, Jerry wheedled that Jailer into letting him put a phone call through to Los Angeles, collect. And he took a desperite chance on not being overheard, as he mumbled quietly to the Dentist who he was, and where he was at, and the predicimint he was in.

 The Studio finally dwelved into Histry for Mommy and came up with George Sand, the well-known Tomboy.

162

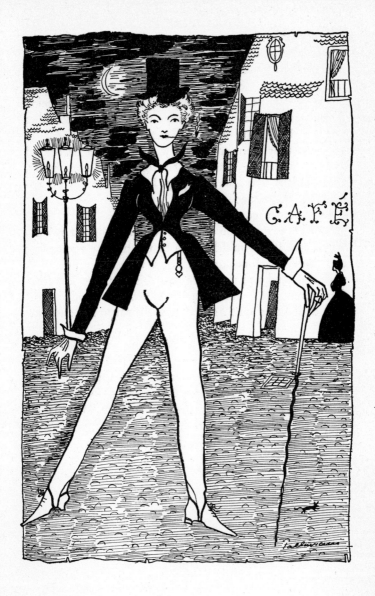

Well, luckily that Dentist was the one person in the whole World able to recognize Jerry's lisp. So he dashed out to the Dessert, with Bail Money, and a razor, and one of Jerry's Cowboy Outfits. And at night, under cover of darkness, he drove Jerry back to Los Angeles, going past miriads of newsboys who were skreetching out the Head Lines of his dissapearince. But they finally got into that Dentists Office without being deteckted and, by working Night and Day for twenty-four hours, that Dentist was able to equip Jerry Jones for his romantick reapearince.

But, before going on with the picture, Jerry made Mommy a propasition that he wouldn't contest my divorce case if I would let him blame me for wandering out there, all alone, on the Dessert, in communication with the Sand and the Stars, over his Hopeless Love for Mrs. Jones, the Famous Star of Montaigne Productions, who drove men mad and made them eager for destruction.

Well, I hated to risk ruining my reputation and harming the investmint Leo's Studio had made in me, but I told Jerry to go ahead and do it. Only when his statemint came out, it was a Boom-erang on Jerry. Because the Publick had grown to admire Mommy so much that they loved to think I could ruin the Life of a ruggid Westerner like Jerry Jones.

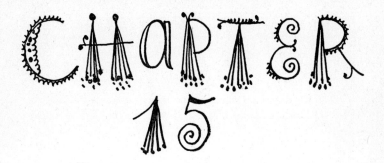

CHAPTER 15

Well, after Jerry and I finished our co-starring ve-
hicle and returned to Hollywood, he was so releeved to
think he'd never have me around any longer for com-
petition, that he behaved like a little lamb and even
helped pack up my things. And although he felt that
any wife who was accustimed to his collossal Ranch
House ought to publicize our separation by going to
the best hotel, he finally gave in, and moved me to the
Cal-U-Met himself, in his own station wagon.

But when Mommy walked, bag and baggige, into the
Lobby of the Cal-U-Met, our Proprietor, Mr. Berry,
couldn't believe his eyes. For up to that momint, the
most famous Guests the Cal-U-Met had ever had, had
only been Bit Players. So Mr. Berry welcomed me with
open arms, and everything started out lovely. For even
the old bedroom Mommy used to occupy was vacant.

Only I had hardly finished unpacking before the Montaigne Publicity Departmint heard where I was at, and
called up to tell me I must imediately vacate, because
they had just rented a furnished House (compleet with

Butler, Cook, and maids, and a Swimming Pool, and a Projection Room, and a Limousine, and a Chaufeure) to illustrate a feeture story they had planted with the Fan Magazines, which was to be entitled, "EFFIE HUNTRISS GIVES HER FIRST 'AT HOME.'"

Well, I asked permission to remane at the Cal-U-Met that night because Mr. and Mrs. Berry were giving me a "Welcome Home" party, in the Coffee Shoppe. But the Departmint was adamint, so I had to acquience.

But when I tried to explane it to the Berrys, they had already ordered the Cake, and it was plain to see they felt I had become erratick. (So I was rapidly learning that one of the worse things Fame can do to a Star, is to make you hurt the feelings of persons you would like to be fond of.)

Well, Mommy's first Cocktail Party was a great success, with all the Magazine Writers reeling around a home they publicized as expressing Mommy's own individuality.

But a home of my own complicated everything, in every respeckt. Because when my first Personal Maid asked Mommy where she could find my underwear, I didn't have the courage to say I felt the California Climate made it optional. So I told a Fibb, and said I lost it, which caused that Maid to go to Magnins and buy me a whole outfit. And, to save Mommy's face, I had to put on lingeray.

And after I ultimitely got married to a really nice person, like Lester, home life was sometimes iritating. Because even Mommy's marriage to Lester only turned out to be a long series of misunderstandings. For he had been so wild over Mommy from the start, that I felt it would of been unpolite to not seem like I retallyated. And then, one night, Lester was taken by surprize when he suddenly caught Mommy, off guard, yawning. So Lester demanded a "Show-Down." But the arguemint turned out to be the most understanding talk I ever had with any Husband, up to that time. Because after Lester heard my side of the story, he opologized from the bottom of his Heart, for inadvertintly causing Mommy two whole years of boredom and dissimilation.

And that night, for the first time since we met, Lester and I suddenly found ourselves laughing together. Because, for two years, I had put over a perfeck performance on Lester, when every Movie Critic in the Country claimed that Mommy would never in my Life learn how to act.

So from then on, Lester and I became the best of Friends. And when he started to take an interest in Gracie Kay, I was the first one he ran to, with the news that Gracie recipricated, without any shadow of a doubt.

But after Lester moved away and married Gracie, I used to often-times be lonesome. And then I would start to think about my own Real Mother, and wonder whether she could be alive, somewheres, without ever knowing that the famous Effie Huntriss was her own flesh and blood. For the only means she could of had to know we were related was by recognizing the Name I receeved when I was adopted. But when I first went to work at Pinnacle, Danny Todd thought Mommy's name was dull, so he offered a Prize of Five Dollars for a substitoot. Well, the Contest was won by his Office

Boy, Moe Klein, who wanted to Christen Mommy "Wilda Huntriss." But I felt that adding "Wilda" to the "Huntriss" was reaching too far, so I ensisted on retaneing my own first name (which Dadda's Wife had given me, because she felt that any girl called "Effie" could never get in trouble). So Danny admitted that the two Names cancelled one another out, and might succeed in being prevocitive.

Well, one night when I was laying alone in bed feeling blue, I suddenly realized it was Sunday, and I was on the verge of missing Louella's Broadcast. So I turned the Radio on, and the sound of her voice soon started sootheing Mommy. And then, like a flash, there came to my mind a way to find out if my real Mother was alive, and if so, how to get in touch with her. Because for a long while Louella had wanted to announce Mommy's real Name on her Sunday Broadcast and I suddenly realized the momint she did it, Mothers would begin to crop up in every direction, one of which might be authentick.

So Monday morning I called up the Head of our Publicity Departmint, Rupert Collins, to get his permission. But Rupert was in no mood to let Louella do it. Because up to that time, all Mommy had had in the way of Relatives had been Husbands who were inveteran trouble-makers. So Rupe made Mommy promise to drop the whole idear.

But the following week was full of Agent-Trouble, and Servant-Trouble, and Script-Trouble, and Director-Trouble, and even Fiancee-Trouble. (For I had had to start going places with a talky Author, who was always having "notions" which he mistook for "idears.")

So I kept dreaming how lovely it would be, to have a Mother I could run to, and never be forced to marry anybody, any more, just in order to not be left alone.

Well, by Saturday Night, Mommy was so lonesome that I found myself going to a Premeer with that pompis Script Writer. And after lissening to his Dialogue throughout the Picture, I made up my mind to take a drastic step. So the momint I got home, I phoned Louella and told her to go ahead and broadcast my real name. (For sometimes it gives a Star a feeling of Contra-Irritation to play with fire.)

Well, the repercushions of that Broadcast began early Monday morning, for Rupert Collins phoned Mommy to report to him, in the Publicity Departmint, the momint I got on the Lot. And when I stepped into his Office, Rupe was in a Fuhrer. For his branch of Publicity was not so much to have infoamation about us Stars get out, as it was to see that it didn't *leak* out. And facts of that type have got bottled up in Rupert, year after year, and caused him to be imbittered.

So Mommy had to set there and lissen, while Rupe told how he was forced to guard our secrets so digilintly that he didn't even dare to share the same bedroom with his own Wife, for fear he might murmur something in his sleep. And he told Mommy that only the day before, he had had to scheem like a veritable Mike E. Ovelli, trying to suppress a pair of un-planned Fatherhoods that had been trumpted up on the French Riviera against the husband of one of America's foremost Sweethearts.

Well, Rupert's veehimince caused Mommy to begin to worry. And in no time at all, I realized he was right.

Because the most mortifying type of "Relatives" started pouring into Hollywood. And those of the Female Gender who were either too young, or too old, to be "Mothers" were "Grandmas," "Sisters," "Cousins," and "Aunties." And the men claimed to be every Relation that the Masculine Gender can boast of.

Well, although we Film Stars keep our Address a secret, any "Relative" who has a Dollar, can always buy a ticket on a Sight-Seeing Bus, where the Bus Driver points our Residence out to them. And, of course, the next step is for the "Relative" to get off the bus, and ring the front door bell, and announce their Relationship to our Butlers, who then step back to the telephone, and announce them to the Police, who have organized a Special Squawd to pick them up.

But one of those "Relatives," Little Mouse, turned out to actually be your Mommy's own, authentick Momma, who picked up Louella's Broadcast in a Motel at Miami. So, as fast as hitch-hikeing could get her acrost the Continint, your Grandma came running.

Well, in cases where Relatives haven't got the dollar for a Sight-Seeing Ticket, they go straight to the Studio, and try to get past the Policemen on the Gate (who are specially chosen for their ability to be adamint). So the day Momma showed up, the Gate was guarded by Officer Shawn, who had been forced to dispense with so many of my false Relations that he had grown more skeptic than usual. So, on looking Momma over, he felt her resimblince to me might be purely co-incidintal. Because so many persons tried to look like me that, naturally, once in a while, somebody succeeded, to some extint.

But Momma had so much charm that she could talk her way around a whole Hollywood Police Squawd (and subsequintly sometimes did). So Officer Shawn, after restraining some of the most expert Gate Crashers in the whole World, finally gave your Grandma his arm and escorted her in to our Studio's Cheef of Police, Shep Newcombe.

Well, in order to study Momma and find out if she had enough evidents to prove her contintion, Cheef Newcombe envited her to have a cup of coffee. And Momma charmed Cheef Newcombe in the Comissary even more than Officer Shawn, because he was more of a Lady's Man. So he was consequintly entransed when Momma showed him a Receept she had got from my Foster Parents when they first took me (which to that day she never knew how she hung onto, in her transient life of following the Horses).

Well, Cheef Newcombe asked to be excused and hurried over to Rupe's office to produce the evidents that proved Momma's authenticity. And while Rupe set at his desk and studied it, Cheef Newcombe raved over Momma, as a Relative who would occupy a warmer place in the Heart of the Publick than any of my Husbands ever had. But Rupe meerly remarked that Husbands could be paid off, and got rid of, while Mothers are here to stay. But he said he might as well get over to the Comissary and look the situation squarely in the face.

 Mommy's Producers finally took me back to the days of lighter-weight dress fabricks.

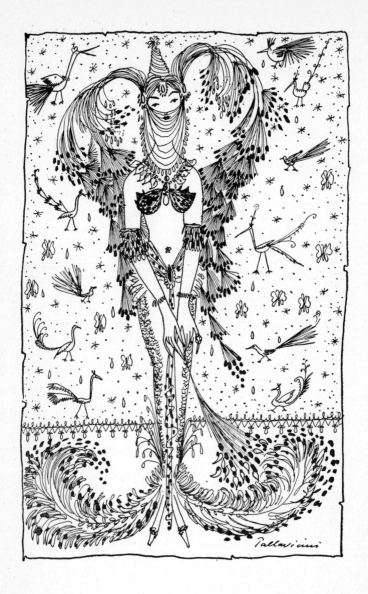

But on reaching there, it develliped that the momint Cheef Newcombe left Momma alone, she had gone to another table and intraduced himself to Red Skelton, Eukalali Ike, the late Ted Healy, and the Ritz Brothers. For if there was one thing your Grandma loved even more than Romance, it was Laughter. So, as Rupe walked through that door, he caught her setting in the center of a Groop who were Intra-nationally famous for amuseing the Publick. But it was Momma who was amuseing *them*.

Well, one good look at Momma was all Rupe needed to decide she was a case for Executive Action by the Head of the Studio, Hobart K. Hass, himself. So he ensisted on dragging Momma away from the coterry she had accumilated, and, accompanied by Cheef New-combe (who needed no second invitation to tag along), Rupe escorted Momma to the Executive Bungaloo to make the Aununciation.

But on getting there Rupe decided he had better prepare Mr. Hass for the shock. Because the feelings H.K. has for Motherhood are more sacred than anybody else's in the whole Film Industry. So Rupe turned Momma over to a Minor Executive in the outer office and preceeded into H.K.'s Inner Sanctim.

Well, when H.K. heard the news that Effie Huntriss had a Mother, he was flabber-ghasted. For it was a pe-culiar co-incidince that I was on a Sound Stage that very momint in the midst of shooting a script about a Mother and Child who, after many years, were re-united.

Well, H.K. is such an inveteran Lover of Great Scenes in Real Life that he told Cheef Newcombe to rush out on the Lot and bring me to his office without explaneing the reason. And then H.K. ordered Edna Vaughan Versham to come in, and watch the Sceen of Reconcilliation, so she could steal some additional dialogue from Real Life that might add to the very similitood of her Script.

And then H.K. began to outline a Press Campaign to Rupe, which would exploit Momma, as having lived and breathed in fear that her lost child might be starving somewheres in some gutter, or perhaps even of got into a situation that was censhurable. And when Mr. Hass came to the part where Mommy would kneel at her bed-post every night, and pray for some inkling as to where her child was, H.K. got right down on his own knees and said a Prayer that brought tears to his own eyes while he was ad-libbing it.

But by that time Rupe decided he better interrupt and warn H.K. about your Grandma. So he told H.K. that they could hand her over to the Make-Up Departmint, and let them work on her for hours, and then pose her like Whistler's Mother, but she'd still find some means to turn the whole thing into "Cheesecake."

Well, at that momint, I entered H.K.'s Inner Sanctim with Cheef Newcombe, so Mr. Hass preceeded to overlook Rupe's warning and began to stage the Sceen as if he had been Cecil B. DeMille. For at his right side, he set me. And at the other side, Edna Vaughan Versham. And he set Cheef Newcombe in the background, while Rupe (who is so nervous he has not set down for years) stood up. And then H.K. buzzed the buzzer, and with tear-filled eyes ordered Momma to be ushered in.

Well, as soon as H.K. recovered from his first glimpse of Your Grandma, he rose up with reverince and said, ". . . Effie, dear, this Lady is . . . your Mother!"

And as I stood there, looking at her, in a daze, Momma said, sociably,

"Hello, pal!"

Well, I didn't know what to reply. But the tears were rushing in riverlettes down the cheeks of Mr. Hass, so I didn't want to dissapoint him by saying something that was inadequint.

And then, like a flash, there flashed before my eyes, some of Edna Vaughan Versham's dialogue, just as it was mimyographed in Mommy's Script. So I repeated it (and I quote),

"Oh, Mother . . . I'm afraid I'll never live up to . . . to . . . the Dreams you've had, through all these years, about . . . your little girl! . . ."

But Your Grandma, who could always be counted on to do the wrong thing, replied,

"Don't give it a second thought, honey! Why I wouldn't even of had you, if a certain Roller Coaster I tried out had done its stuff."

So Momma's Dialogue never got into the Script, and we were forced to retain it the way Miss Versham wrote it, with Momma saying,

"Oh, darling . . . darling . . . You're just as I've always dreamed you would be!" (And, as steel flies to a Magnate, Mother and Child are in each other's arms.)

And the upshoot of H.K.'s expirimint was that he envited Momma to go out rumba-ing with him, and ordered Rupe to keep it out of the Papers.

But that was only the beginning, Little Mouse, of

what it means for a Star to have a Mother, Off-the-Screen, in Hollywood. For by the time six months had passed, she caused Rupe Collins to start walking with a stoop.

And, insted of setteling down with me, at Home, Momma started to develop outside Hobbies. And sometimes the Hobby was buying a highly exceptional Trailer, and sometimes it became a Yacht, or a Ranch on the San Fernando Boulevard, or else an Estate in Holmby Hills. But when your Grandma lived in a Trailer, she idealized her Chaufeure. And then, when the Studio would lure her off onto a Yacht, she'd start to dramatize some Boatswain. So then they'd try a Ranch, and it became a Cow-Hand. And when they bribed Momma indoors, she fell under the spell of some Butler.

So the wide diversity of Momma's escorts sometimes made me curious about Somebody who must of been my Daddy. But the stories Momma spun about Husbands used to deeviate so widely that I finally gave up trying to find out who he was.

But whether your Grandma's interest was in Chaufeures or Sea-Fairers, or Over-See'ers, or Major Doma's, I could always count on them being photogenique. So they were always being shot, posed with one arm around your Grandma. And the pictures always got into the papers just when I happened to be playing some roll which required a Press Campaign to proove that my family life was conservatif. (Which is one of the things that drives Publicity Staffs in Hollywood nearly ensane. For no sooner does some Star begin to portray some Saint, than their Husbands start applying for divorces, and mentioning their Fiancees, by name.)

But none of Momma's Escorts ever seemed to think the Salary I paid them was enough. So they were always calling on me for a Bonus. And their demands finally made me so nervous that I had to start taking phena-barbitels, to quieten me down, and benzadrines to put me on my feet again, so I could get to work.

But at last your Grandma luckily started to learn Occultism. And the Studio ordered our Legal Department to make a Deal with her Occult Teacher, to escort her to India. Well, she had been desireous for a long time to take a lengthy trip, so she jumped at the oppertunity. And I set up a Trust Fund for her, with checks payible to a Guaranteed Trust Company at Cal Cutta. And that's where she is now, I guess, because sometimes I get a Post Card from her at Christmas.

But I always felt greatful to her for one thing, which was her attitude towards a Daughter. Because the Mothers of most Film Stars ensist on being emotional over them, during every waking hour. And my Heart used to ache for poor Bunny Ambrose, who would work all day long on a Sound Stage, playing some Emotional Sceen with a Mother professionally, only to have the Real One, waiting on the side-Lines, to start the whole thing going again as soon as Bunny stepped off the Set, and then carry on, in their own Home, without anybody in the way of an Audience.

So when I said Good-bye to your Grandma, we shook hands with the greatest respeck for one another. And I always feel that if we had only both held the same attitude towards the men, we might of had something to base a closer relationship on.

Chapter
16

Well, now, Little Mouse, Mommy is coming to the time when I first incountered your Daddy, and learned that the Dream I had dreamed all my Life, of being held in respeckt by somebody, was capabil of coming true. And I met Clyde Babcock when I was extraordinarily in need of comfort because of something that had happened to Leo Montaigne. For Film Executives in Hollywood have developed two Occupational Diseases (which are, namely, Ulcers of the Stommach and Cardiac of the Heart). And Leo's Studio had ampilly supplied him with the latter.

But beside the greef we all felt when Leo had to give up work and retire, I knew his departure was going to harm the Career of every one of us, encluding Mommy. For the Films Leo Montaigne produced with me caused laughter, on account of being bumptious. But the ones which those other Producers concockted, meerly leered. And nothing is less entertaining than a leer.

And when they tried to change my type one time, by having me play a serious roll in a dramatic Picture, the Producer shot eight reels of Mommy feeling sorry for myself. For those Producers never seem to learn that self-pity is inveritably boresome.

But, in the Heart of Leo Montaigne, there was a great Compassion for Human Beens. So he felt that, when they paid their hard-earned money to get into Moving Picture Theatres, he wanted them to be entertained. And he never thought it was incombrint to exploit anybody's opinion, or to prove something, or other. (Such as the case where our Govermint caught Script Writers trying to prove that "Left" is "Right".) So a Montaigne Production was inveritably a Success. But it was at a terribil cost to Leo.

And Mommy remembers setting with him in the Projection Room one day looking at some Rushes for a Costume Picture that had been shot by his foremost Director. But in a Sceen where an English Duchess was holding a Ball for Royalty, the Hostess was garbed in an afternoon gown with a high collar and long sleeves. And when Leo asked why she wasn't in evening dress, his Director replied, with integritty,

"Look here, Leo, our Script states that this Duchess is a nice woman. And no nice old lady, in my books, would show her bare skin in publick."

Well, that whole sequince had to be shot over again, which was very expensive because the Director, himself, got $7,500 a week. And it was only one example of the struggle Leo went through, year after year, with

Directors, and Stars, and Script Writers, and the Wardrobe Departmint, and the National Board of Review, trying to make his Films look feesible. So finally a terrible day came when he suffered his first Attackt. And six weeks later, the last blow fell on Leo, in his Dessert Retreet at Palm Springs. And the next afternoon came the most unbearible momint in Mommy's Life (up to that time) when we all gathered in Leo's Cinegog, and said good-bye to him, and knew there would never be anybody else to take his place.

Well, after that, your Mommy was handed over to the type of Film Producers who, to quote Skip Norton, were "Foes to entertaimint." And the first of those Productions was made on the Medalion Lot, where Mommy's own Studio had traded me in exchange for Jimmy Durante and a Technicolor Comitmint.

Well, up to the day I first met Clyde Babcock, I had only seen him at a distance, in Romanoffs or Chasens. But just because you happen to see some "Stranger Acrost a Crowded Room" in Hollywood is no cryterion you're ever going to meet him "Again and again." For Social Life in Hollywood moves in cleeks, with the most importint Cleek in those days circulating around "The Montaignes" and another around "The Selznicks," and another around "The Warners," and another around "The Zanucks," etc. etc. So Clyde Babcock's cleek and mine had never seemed to collide.

Well, the morning I arrived at Medalion for the first time was very exciting. And when Mommy drove my car up, I could even tell from the expressions of the Policemen on the Gate that the whole Studio was speculating about the outcome. For I had just been declared free, by the Courts, from Lester and hadn't had time yet to get my name hooked up to annybody else.

Well—that morning was a momentis occasion in more ways than one. For, as Mommy pulled my roadster up to check in, Skip Norton was standing in front of the Main Gate, where he instantaneously became Mommy's Friend (and my interoduction into Unity, when I learned to know him better). For Skip's religious principals are not vizual on the surface and they frequintly come as a surprize.

Well, Skip gets his Nick-Name from the fact that he is of such a nervous temperamint that no move he ever makes has any continuity. And, when Skip is entering a door, he always has to quickly open and close it three or four times, before he finally succeeds in compleeting the entry. And Skippy uses the same preceedure when walking up a flight of steps, by going up and down the first step unnumerable times before he can work up enough momentim to attain the second. And when Skip wants to get into his car (which supplies him with the obsticles of both a door *and* a step) the preceedure is full of suspense as to whether he will ever actually make it.

But in his Dialogue, Skip attains even less continuity than he does in action. For he talks very fast, in a sort of Short-Hand, by leaving out words and connections, so that very few persons ever find out what Skip is actually saying. But any remark he makes is well worth the translation.

For Skip got his education by being a Delivery Boy for a Bootlegger in the Fabilis Twenties and he learned Psychology from Life itself, which is a far cry from the kind that's trumpted up to meet the extingincies of some Film Plot.

Only when Skip tries to get some Producer to insert Psychology into some Script, his humorous delivery causes them to laugh it off, while Authors like Edna Vaughan Versham, who utter fallicys with a flourish, can empress Producers and easily win the Acadimy Award. For the Motion Picture Acadimy is timorous of Talent and doesn't dare to recognize ability that's too outstanding (which is the reason why Will Rodgers, and Charlie Chaplin and W. C. Fields never received any Oscars).

Well, the momint Skip Norton recognized Mommy at the Main Gate, his greeting was as cordial as if we had known one another for years. And without ever hesitating for breath-control Skip hollered at Mommy and said,

"Hel-lo, Effs, my friend! You're a whale of a broad! The whole Lot's waiting to see who you team up with! Most of our male talent belongs in bottles, so watch your step, pal! Look out for Babcock! The son-of-a-bitch walks on his hands to save shoe leather! Never set foot in that sled of his! Its got no breaks! He stops it by running over a piece of chewing gum! And stay out of his shack! When you slam the front door, the roof falls in! Its located next to a chow house! Every time you put your head out the window, the Chef bastes it! I don't claim he's got a swelled head, but they could shoot *Ben Hur* on the rim of his hat."

Well, while Mommy was laughing at Skip, there were unnumerable faces poking out of every front window in the Producers Building, for Story Conferences at

Medalion would of been pretty dull without Skip to listen to.

Well, I thanked Skip for his advice, and, as I was driving through the Gate, he hollered after Mommy and said,

"I just read that Script they're tossing you into! Steel yourself, honey! Its a bowl of worms! They could knit a more thrilling plot in a Yarn Shoppe! Good luck, Pal —hope you stay with us longer than Gohnnerhea in the Early Nineties."

So Mommy laughed again and began to feel at ease, for no matter what happened to me on a strange Lot, I knew I had a Friend in Skippy.

Well, that morning when Mommy's Director, Mr. Hendricks, came to the dressing room to pay his respecks and ask for his date that evening, I thanked him for his courtesy. But I always like to do things according to Hoyle, so I naturally said,

"Mr. Hendricks, don't you feel that the Star has precedents?"

So Mr. Hendricks agreed and gallantly escorted Mommy to the Set. But from the momint I was interaduced to Mr. Babcock, he disregarded Mommy's whole existince, which was such a novel attitude that, after a couple weeks, it finally became provocitive.

But then there came a day when we were off on Location, in a hay field at Sunland, shooting a vialent Love Sceen in the aperture of a hay stack. But just as our Director had succeeded in establishing the required mood, it began to rain, and he said we'd take an hour off for lunch. But it was lovely and dry in that hay stack, so I told the Property Boy I'd remane where I was, if he would kindly bring my box-lunch over to me.

Well, just as I was opening it up, I suddenly noted your Daddy, with his own box-lunch in his hand, coming over towards that hay stack, through the rain. So I felt worried. For the locale I was in might of prompted any man to act flippint, and I hated him to lose the feeling of reserve he had built up. But he first stopped outside the hay stack, and formilly asked if he could join me. And when I, equally formilly, told him to make himself at home, his behavior was even a little bit stiff.

So then your Daddy and I started luncheon and he preceeded to tell me that the day he saw me knitting a Bobby Sock, on the Set, for one of my favorite Fans, he realized I was diferent from what my Publicity had led him to suspect. So I smiled and asked if he had ever had any occasion to believe his own Publicity. And then he smiled too.

Well, when both members of a two-some start to laugh over the same material, it develops a very warm feeling, especially if they happen to be alone in a hay stack when its raining. So before I realized, I suddenly found myself explaneing to Clyde Babcock how, in spite of my Publicity, and the fact my name is a sinbolism for Sex Apeal, I have never associated it in private Life with entertaimint. For to me it has always seemed hum-drum at best, and, at the worst, obnoxious.

Well, then Clyde became very curious and wanted to know if I had never fell in love. So I explained that I did, but it was always idealistically, for the Romance of it. Or else to hold hands with someone who was strong, because I craved to be cherished. Or, when things eventually went wrong, to be cajoled.

And then, to prove my point, I recited a quotation from Shakespeare (which I had learned from a Dramatic Coach the day I took a lesson once, in acting) that went,

> *Tell me where is Fancy Bread,*
> *In the Heart or in the Head? . . .*
> *Reply . . . reply.*

And I told your Daddy I could reply that, in my case, it is mentol.

Well, I had never mentioned anything like that before, to anyone but Lalla (who had utterly failed to know what I was talking about). But your Daddy understood, and was apreciative, because he had been going places for months with Carmen Dolores, as a publicity requiremint, and had been hectored by her behavior being constintly frantick.

Well, by that time the rain had stopped and the Camera Crew was moving up, so our conversation had to end. But for several days after that, your Daddy respecktfully refrained from trying to date Mommy, and he continued to address me as "Miss Huntriss" and behave like I was prim. So I leave it to my Mouse to figure out who Mommy started in to dream about, at night.

And then one morning I read in the *Reporter* that Carmen Dolores had gone to Mexico City to visit her sick Grandma. So I felt the item might be followed by repercushions. And I was right, for that afternoon,

186

while we were shooting a sequince where your Daddy
caught me taking a Bubble Bath, he asked for his first
date. And it was for nothing less than to go to the
Hollywood Bowl, for a Concert!

Well, when we reached the vicinity of the Bowl that
evening, your Daddy wanted to preteck me from being
suffercated by my Fans while he was paying for tickets,
so he dispensed with buying any. But he led Mommy up
a path, along the hillside which forms the distint edge of
the Bowl. And your Daddy and Mommy stayed there in
the bushes, under the Stars, lissening to Stocowski play
Bock. But he didn't try to even so much as take
Mommy's hand.

And he didn't do it the next week, either, when we
went back to the same spot, to watch the Fantasy of
A Midsummer's Night's Dream, which asks the audience
to believe that a girl could fall in love with a donkey.

But when we attended the last night at the Bowl,
setting there on our hillside, Clyde said he had written
me something, which he was going to recite during the
solo of Yehoody Manoonin. For he wanted to hear how
he sounded to the tones of an adequint violinist.

Well, your Daddy's poem was so beautiful that I
learned it by Heart. And it went like this:

> *How do I love thee? Let me count the ways*
> *I love thee to the depth, and breath, and height,*
> *My soul can reach.*
> *I love thee to the level of every day's*
> *Most quiet need, by sun and candle-light.*
> *I love thee freely, as men strive for right;*
> *I love thee purely, as they turn from praise.*

(And although I naturally suspected it must of been written by someone who was more of an expert at poems than your Daddy, it would of broke the spell to realize I knew. And spells are so infrequint, in Life, that I tried to only think of the great curtesy your Daddy paid me, as a man of his vaunted integritty, who hated falsehood.)

Well, the next step was to try and turn Mommy's Dream into Reality. And by that time the Bowl Concerts were over, so on our next date, when your Daddy was driving me towards a Drive-In for Dinner, I told him that I would always ensist on paying half of every check. So he suddenly swerved his car around, and said it was high time for us to be seen eating a glamrous meal, at Romanoffs. So I knew I must of hit on the right preceedure.

Well, we started having cocktails that night, in a boothe at Romanoffs. And Mommy soon had the courage to bring up the subjeck of Matrimony and say I wanted to be a Self-Supporting-Wife, and even sign a paper to that extent. And I have never seen anything like the releef on your Daddy's face. For he had fallen in love too, but, up to that momint, he had not been able to think of a solution to all the problims it entailed. So he started ordering Champagne to celebrate.

Well, we set there making plans, until the waiter finally brought it to our notice that we were the last customers in Romanoffs. So we left. But we didn't feel like we could drag ourselves apart, so Clyde ensisted on whisking me over to Barney's Beanery, where we set until daylight, without even noting the hardness of those stools, and talked. And then, suddenly, we thought about Louella. So we went into the phone boothe, to wake her up, and tell her the news of our engagemint.

Well, Louella was thrilled. But since it was only Tuesday, she said,

"Can I count on you two children to keep apart for the rest of the week, so I can spring it as a scoop on my Sunday Broadcast?"

So we promised we would. And then I made your Daddy step outside the boothe, while I whispered a secret to Louella which I was too dividint to let anybody know. For the secret was that I even wanted to have a Little Mouse, by Clyde.

Well, the next Sunday evening we set hand in hand on Mommy's back veranda and it was the greatest thrill I ever had to hear Louella saying,

"My First Exclusive! . . . Effie Huntriss is in love again, and this time it's the Real Thing. This time it's Clyde Babcock, and seeing that both of them have their Final Decrees, it looks like Wedding Bells soon, for Effie and Clyde. And here's a secret a little bird has told me. For the first time in her Life, Effie really *wants* to have a baby. So this time it looks permanint. Good luck, Clyde and Effie, and lots and lots of little ones."

Well, Louella's Broadcast was relayed to Mexico City, so the next day we had to escape from Carmen Dolores by eloping to Yuma.

CHAPTER 17

Well, Little Mouse, the time is drawing near, now, when you can be expected any instint. But with Vernon away all day at work, we seem to be finding ourselves alone a great deal. For Peoria finished polychroming the whole house several weeks ago, and she has begun to be bored. So she frequintly trumpts up an excuse to run out, and takes her Autograph Book, and gets on the Bus, and goes milling around other neighborhoods, to contackt other Stars, and stays away for hours.

But while waiting for the Mouse, alone, I have started to think about something I have never breathed to anybody, not even your Daddy. Because when I first suspected there was going to be a Mouse, I wanted to be very conservatiff and not take any chances. So I gave up the Chinese Herb Doctor everyone was patrinizing then, and went to Dockie Davis. Well, Dockie ensisted on going through Mommy's personal Life, and found a flaw in my condition (which had resulted from the time Lester had been forced to rush me to the Cedars of Lebanon, to get rid of a racking back-ache by my operation).

Well, when Dockie learned about that episode, he said it deprived me of having my Mouse without danger. And he wanted to imediately tell Clyde. But I knew how half-hearted your Daddy was anyhow, and that one more excuse would make him decide Mommy shouldn't risk going through with it. So I begged Dockie not to tell him and finally Dockie gave in and promised he would help me all he could.

But last week I decided it would cheer me up to tell Vernon the squalms I was beginning to have, about having my Mouse with safety.

But it always upsets Vernon to get on any subjeck that's vital. For Vernon is like all his type of persons, who are capabil of handeling any antagonist they can call names to. (And I had to laugh the day they were going to shut the phone off, because he had the time of his Life calling the Telephone Corporation "a lousy flock of nickel grabbers." And he even got them to leave the phone in, by telling how Mommy was going to need it any momint, to get hold of Dockie Davis.)

But Mommy had no sooner mentioned my dark thoughts than I realized they were more than poor Vernon could take. So I tried to avince a greater cheer-

 In the Three-Million-Dollar Production called La Pompadore, your Mommy portrayed a world-famous French Madam.

fulness, but I could see I had ruined the Home Life he and I enjoyed together. For Vernon started to be late for dinner every day and came in frequintly with liquor on his breath.

Well, Saturday night Vernon never came Home at all (which was the first time I ate a dinner concockted by Peoria and found out to what an extint she has neglected her cookery). So the next day was Sunday, and the momint Peoria served breakfast, she went trapseing off, on her regular tour of Churches, to see Pat O'Brien pass the plate for Catholics and Ginger Rogers lay-read for Christian Science.

But in the afternoon while I was laying here alone (feeling my Little Mouse alive and kicking) I thought I heard Vernon come in. So I lissened. And when I actually heard him on the stairs I began to worry, for fear he might be the worst for liquor and upset my Mouse. So, with difficulty, I set up. But when Vernon stepped through the door, there didn't seem to be a single sign he had been drinking, although, at the same time, he spoke very excited, when he said,

"I've got that Witch downstairs who committed petty larceny on Babcock."

(And so, all the while Mommy thought Vernon had forgot us, he had valiantly spent his time trying to round up an Antagonist he could call defanate names to. And it was Inga Swansen.)

Well, Mommy started in to quake, and ask what I should do, or what I could say to her. But Vernon told me to meerly use my own intooition, and then he hectically dashed downstairs, to tell her to come up.

Well, I had played the Sceen I was going to have to

go through unnumerable times in Pictures, but it was always I who played the Temptriss. So I hardly knew how to interprit it from the opasite angle. And I wondered how much the Sceen was going to differ, this time, from Miss Versham's Scripts.

Well, it began to differ the momint Inga Swansen merged through the doorway. Because insted of Mommy reveeling mingelled emotions of outrage and dignity, all I could do was meerly look at her, agog. But there she stood, without any Make-Up on, dressed meerly in slacks and a turtle necked Sweater, and she made Mommy feel, with all the spangles on my bed jacket, as if I looked hum-drum. And I couldn't find my tongue, to even say "Good Afternoon." So then she started to speak, herself, in a voice that was very deep and very slow, and said,

"Its nice to meet you in the flesh, Miss Huntriss."

But still Mommy couldn't even find the two words to say "Thank you." So then she started to gaze around the room and said,

"You have a very bright Home, Miss Huntriss, with so much gold everywhere."

And while I was still not able to thank her for the complimint, she pretended to be vague and said,

"Please tell me why that nice young friend of yours made me come up here. What is this Mystry?"

Well, finally I gained voice enough to answer her and said,

"I guess Vernon brought you here so we could talk about Clyde Babcock, my husband."

Well, the next words she spoke made it seem like she

was trying to make your Daddy look trivvial, because she said,

"Oh! So he's your husband, the little man?"

Well, Mommy said "Yes," but I had to bridle, for Clyde is anything but little, physically.

And then it began to look like she was trying to make trouble for your Daddy, because the next thing she said was,

"Why didn't he mention that he had a wife?"

Well, Mommy knew that he had mentioned it. For with Clyde's preclivity to talk, he would of had to tell her everything, or else run out of conversation. But I knew there was no time to waste quibbeling, for I could feel my Mouse begin to stir.

So without minceing any words I said,

"Miss Swansen, do you intend to marry my husband?"

Well, at first Mommy's question didn't seem to filter through her brain. But when it finally did, she said,

"Oh, now, Miss Huntriss! Isn't Life complicated enough without forever getting married? Why do you Americans distress yourselves with such idears?"

Well, I knew she was striking at the very Heart of American Matrimony, so I pulled up as straight as I could, and answered,

"Because Marriage in the United States is sacred!"

But then her eyelashes only got wider apart, and she respondid,

"And do you think the marriage of Mr. Babcock and yourself is sacred?"

Well, Mommy wanted to answer as best I could, but the only thing I could think up to say was,

"Clyde must of cared for me very much, to of fallen in love again, after all his divorces."

But then she only smiled and said,

"Men always keep on trying to be lovers. But it doesn't mean they succeed, any more than if they tried to paint pictures and never become artists. Or write poems and never get to be poets."

And then she came over to the bed and set down beside Mommy and said,

"But the sad thing about Life is that we women are diferent. We are all poets. Otherwise how could we bear to stand men?"

Well, I didn't know what to respond, because she sounded plausibil. So then she said,

"Your husband will never be able to love anyone, Miss Huntriss, outside his looking glass."

Well, I was so surprised to hear her attackt your Daddy that I couldn't find the words to defend him. And then she went on to say,

"If he had wanted to come back to you, he'd have done it days ago, when I told him to stay away from me because he was a bore."

And while I was setting here stunned to hear that their Romance was finished, Inga looked at Mommy with her Sea-Green Eyes, and smiled. And when Inga smiles like that, it seems as if a person has suddenly been whisked into a peculiar land, where everything strange becomes very plausible. And when Inga spoke again, she said,

"What makes you feel you've ever got to have some clumbsy man around, Miss Huntriss?"

And for a momint her question sounded so reasonable I couldn't think of the reply. But then my Mouse gave me a nudge and I suddenly knew the answer. So I set straight up and told her that my Mouse was going to have its Daddy in the House, no matter how inadequint he was.

Well, when Inga found out I was ademint about your Daddy, she remarked,

"Poor little Miss Huntriss!"

And the next thing I knew, she had left. So I set here, looking after her in a daze, because I realized that Inga Swansen could supply motavation enough to get anybody into trouble. And it was the first momint I compleetly understood your Daddy walking out on us, and whole-heartedly forgave him.

And then I began feeling sorry for Clyde. Because I realized how ashamed he must be to come crawling back home after finding out that he was boresome. So I called for Vernon (who dashed in from the door where he had been lissening) and asked him to get your Daddy on the phone, so I could issue the envitation he was waiting for.

Well, the only person who might know where Clyde was at was our Secretary, so Vernon called Madge up. And when he got her on the phone, we found that Clyde was right there at her apartmint. So I quickly reached for the receever. But before I heard your Daddy's voice, I heard Madge saying to him, in a whisper,

"Don't tell her about us now. The poor thing isn't up to it."

Well, suddenly I started to get cold all over, because Madge's words sounded omnious. So Vernon grabbed the receever away from me and told Clyde in no small terms to say when he was coming home and tell him what the score was. And Mommy put my head close to the phone to lissen.

Well, then your Daddy started to tell Vernon how he had gone through Hell-on-Earth over the cold Heart of Inga Swansen. But he said he didn't feel he could come straight back to me after his defeet with Inga, because it wouldn't win him his Moralle back. For everybody in Hollywood knew he could always come Home. So the only way he could find himself in the dark, was to prove he was capabil of winning somebody who was hard to get. And it was a great challinge for your Daddy to win Madge Mayhew, because she so thoroughly knew all about him.

And then, while Mommy started to feel convulshions coming on, Madge got on the phone and I heard her say to Vernon,

"Look here, Mr. Clark, you know very well that these two Googongs both need keepers. I can't take on both of them, but I have been able to move Clyde in with me, and I've managed to keep him straight since the half-witted business he got into with that Sweede.

"So you can tell Effie I've spent the past few days going over his bugits and regiminting his debts. And as soon as the Baby arrives, I'm going to make him set Effie up in a modest home. And she'll never need worry about the child, because Clyde and I are going to take it and raise it sensibly."

So that was when Vernon had to tell Madge to get the Hell off the phone so he could get ahold of Dockie Davis.

Chapter 18

Well, before Mommy's convulshions got beyond control Dockie arrived here. But it wasn't even yet Mommy's time, so he prescribed some stronger pills to quieten my nerves and gave Vernon instructions that he could be reached all night at a Stag Party Bob Cobb was giving in honor of Maxie Rosenbloom. So I finally drowsed off and everything got very Pieceful.

But yesterday, when Dockie paid his evening call here, his hangover from Bob Cobb's party was still so vialent that he had to take a dose of Mommy's nerve pills, with me. And then, last night, I slept quiet again. And today it was nearly noon before Peoria woke me up, coming in with my breakfast and the *Hollywood Reporter*.

Well, as I looked at Peoria, her face was a mass of smiles, and I asked what had made her so cheery. So she said that the *Reporter* had published something about Mommy, once again, and proudly pointed out a squibb to me, which said,

"What Hollywood Representative of a promanint News Magazine had his nose bashed in when Ace Cutter, Jimmy McCoy, defended ex-screen Star, Effie Huntriss, in a discussion which reached an all time low for case-hardened frigidity?"

Well, I wondered what that Representitive could of said that could of caused Jimmy McCoy to attackt him. And I knew it couldn't of been my acting ability, for if it had been, Jimmy would of indubitably taken the side of the Representitive.

And I knew the fight over me couldn't be personal, because Jimmy has always had a vialent aversion to Film Stars. And the only time your Mommy ever succeeded in getting Jimmy to escort me was once when I inveegled him into taking me to the Brown Derby. But when the mobs in front made me stop to sign autographs, Jimmy was forced to stand and hold my White Fox Fur Wrap. And when the crowd suddenly deserted me for Betty Grable, I looked around for Jimmy, but he was gone, and my bran new white Fox Wrap was wrapped around a fire hydrant.

And the next morning when I went to Jimmy's Cutting Room to opologize, he said that "any man who ever went out with one of we Glamor Girls was nothing but an animated coat wrack." And then he went to work replacing my best Close-Up with an Insert of a telegram that expressed the same thing better and said, "Beat it!"

Well, I finally called up the Studio to try and get ahold of Skip and see if he knew anything about the fight. But everybody was at lunch, so I told the Operator to tell Skip to call me just as soon as he came back.

So then I had to just lay still, and wait. But, laying here, I started worrying for fear, after the Mouse arrives, Madge will go to some Court of Law and tell them things about Mommy that will make them take the Mouse away from me. Like one time, on the Set, when the Director told Mommy to take my jacket off. So I thoughtlessly did, but it caused the spectaters to gasp, because of my preclivity to not wear a blouse or need any brassier.

And Madge could also tell the Court how I had developped the habit of useing vulgerisms when visiters were on the Set. Because meeting Film Stars always makes visiters feel in awe. So I used to think it was only hospitiable to put them at ease by making remarks that let them know we Film Stars are meerly Human.

And then there was the time at the El Morocco, in New York, when Mommy was forced to strike an escort with a candalabrum. And I knew that everybody in that Court Room, encluding Madge, herself, would think it was only right to give my Mouse to Clyde and her.

But finally the phone started to ring. So I took the receever and heard somebody rattling the other receever, off and on, trying to get it to his ear. So I knew it must be Skippy. And sure enough, I finally heard him say,

"Hel-low, my little iffen-giffen! My little Bi-so-dol. What do you maintain, Effie, my friend? What's on the mighty mind?"

Well, I asked Skip to please tell me what had happened yesterday in that fight. But Skip only began to be evasive, and go off on several diferent tangints, and say,

"Effs, you're a helova broad! The whole Lot misses you! But don't come back! What you're producing is never going to be dry! This joint is murder! They're making enough blunders to be in Washington! Saw Pinza yesterday at Perino's! If it weren't for MacArthur, he'd be singing *The Mikado*."

Well, as Skip never runs out of breath, I had to finally break in on him. So I asked why he never came over to see Mommy any more, and he replied,

"*See* you, Effs? Why, I couldn't edge my way through that mob of your Fans with a knife strapped to my elbow."

So I asked Skip what made him think I had a mob of Fans around me? Or anybody else?

And then he said,

"Don't try to kid me, honey! You're talking to the Mighty Skip!"

Well, when I told Skip how long it had been since I entertained my last caller, he was astrounded and started right in to bellow and say,

"I'll be right over, Effie-Boy! I love you."

And then, after many attempts to contackt the receever with the hook, I finally heard him bang it up.

Well, just lissening to Skip on the phone had cheered Mommy up and even made me feel relaxed. So by the time he dashed over to the House, I was dozeing and having a dream that I had come through my ordeel safe and was snuggling my Mouse so close that I could even smell the perfume of its little neck.

204

But Skip woke me up with his yelling, and then, as usual, he started to nervously walk around the room, talking first about one thing, and then another, and breaking up cigarettes, and reaching in his pocket for more, and rattling scraps of paper and fiddeling with the cups of coffee Peoria served him.

But when Skip finally started to go, I told him I couldn't rest in Piece until he told me about that fight Jimmy McCoy had at the Studio. So at last he let himself be pinned down although, as usual, he spoke in double talk, and said,

"Some louse on a News Mag got all gassed up with Doc Davis at Maxie Rosenbloom's party. So yesterday the guy came to the Studio with some copy he wrote about the Mighty Effs. Started heeling around the Barber Shop for more information, and Jimmy hopped out of a Chair and slugged him. So I grabbed the microbe's copy and ran. But it doesn't mean a thing. Dockie had a weeping jag. I've got to go now. Big men waiting for me."

So Skippy stumbled a couple of times over the threshhold and finally got out.

But while Mommy layed there, still poundering over that fight, Peoria began to clean up the debree Skippy had strewn all over the bedroom (consisting of empty cigarette packages, and broken-up cigarettes he never lit, and others he lit and threw away, and lumps of sugar he only half melted in his coffee, and old parking Lot Tickets, and I.O.U.'s). And then I suddenly noted Peoria pick up a piece of typewritten paper, so I asked her to hand it to me.

Well, Little Mouse, it is the article Skippy grabbed

from that Magazine Writer, and run with. And it is what is termed in Newspaper Circles an obituerry, which says (and Mommy quotes),

Obit. "Effie Huntriss, erratic blonde cinemactress; christened Effie Slocum, reared in Kansas City. Ran out on family at 16, destination Hollywood. Sought publicity by appearing in highly censorable Nude Deal. Became the Cinema's number one symbol of Sex with her first Montaigne Production. Deserted first husband, agent Bert Griggsby, at altar. Divorced Second Husband, Jerry Jones, two years later. Third, Lester Cummings, same length of time. Fourth, and current husband, Clyde Babcock. During her last months her name coupled with small time book salesman, Vernon Clark." (Unquote.)

So that squibb indicates that Mommy won't be with my Mouse much longer. But if you are safely born and manage to grow up, Mommy's book will let you know I wasn't nearly as Sexy as the gossip colloms indicated and that I loved my little Mouse with all my heart.

And now I guess Mommy better put my pencil down and call for help.

Chapter 19

Well, Little Mouse, today you are old enough, according to the Order of the Court, to start spending your first six weeks with Clyde and Madge Babcock. And last night, when I started cleaning out an old suit-case, to pack your little things in, a whole assortment of momentos fell out, that Skip Norton sneaked from the Prop Departmint one time, to fix the Mouse an attick up, to play in. But there isn't any attick in our bungaloo, or even any celler, because the San Fernando Valley is so hot a person couldn't set foot in an attick if they had one, and every time it rains, a celler would be flooded.

Well, when Mommy finally reached the bottom of that suitcase, I found the book I never had time to finish since that momentis day, five years ago, when they rushed Mommy to the Cedars of Lebanon, and

Skip got on the phone, and put in an Emergency-Long-Distance Call to Unity Headquarters in Missouri, and got them to hold a Special Concentration of Healing Thoughts that pulled the Mouse and Mommy through that terrible ordeel, safe.

And setting by your little crib tonight Mommy can see now that everything in our Life has its place in Divine Order . . . even Inga Swansen. For when the Film she did with your Daddy got released, the Critics compared her acting ability to Clyde Babcock's mugging. So something inside your Daddy rose to the challinge and, in the following Film he shot, he was able to restrain his mugging. And during his next few pictures your Daddy, somewheres along the line, learned how to act (which is the only Security an actor can ever attain). So he has never run out of good assignmints and his paymint on the Mouse's upkeep never lapses.

But its sometimes hard to see the good in everything the momint it happens. And with the Mouse leaving Mommy tomorrow for the first time since you were born, I won't be able to sleep, so I'm going to set here by your crib, and finish my Book. And as soon as Mommy learns her Mouse how to read, my Book will contradict the things Madge is going to try to say against Hollywood, and me, during those six weeks every year when you have to be with your Daddy.

And while Clyde is playing the roll of my Mouse's Daddy, I'm going to hope and pray he'll give it the best performance of his life. For I have felt from the beginning, that my Mouse should have a man around to emulate. And as soon as I discovered the Mouse was not a little girl, I made poor Vernon move away (because home-enviromint can never begin too early).

And I've always thought that the best man in all of Hollywood for any growing boy to emulate, would be Jimmy McCoy. For when we were having our previous World War, and many a Great Star was behind the Lines, fighting (in the days before T.V.) to bring back Vaudeville, Jimmy was right up at the Front, getting captured at the Battle of the Bulge. And he was so popular with Our Foe, that they made him promise to come back some day, and cover the same terrain socially.

Well, for five years now, Jimmy McCoy has been proposing Matrimony to your Mommy. Because, on that momentis day at the Studio when Jimmy heard in the Barber Shop that Mommy's life was in danger, he suddenly knew that the vialents of his aversion to me, had been caused by trying to combat his disgust over being in love with a Film Star. But after Jimmy gave in to his weakness, he began to enjoy it.

Well, during these whole five years, Mommy's answer to Jimmy's proposals has inveritably been, "No."

Because every time I ask if he respeckts me, all Jimmy does is grin, and say,

"Good Greef! For what?"

So Mommy has always refused him.

But just the same I owe a great deal to Jimmy, because he was the one who won my fight to keep Clyde and Madge from gaining the soul custiddy of my Mouse. For during the Court preceedure all Jimmy had to do was to set in front of your Daddy and make a gesture that was indicative of a pair of sizzors, and Clyde was so worried that Jimmy might start cutting out his Close

Ups, that he agreed to let Mommy have exclusive rights to my Mouse, clear up till its Fifth Birthday.

And it is thanks to Jimmy that I have been able to support my Mouse in comfort all these years. For after the Trial was over, he came to Mommy's ade, by learning me a new Career, where I am not dependint on a Publick which decides, overnight, that you can't act, and suddenly drops you for some new Star (who probably can't act either).

And so now I can pick my Mouse up every morning and tuck him safely into my old, faded-out, Baby-blue Cadilac convertible, and speed off to the Studio, where the Mouse can play with Film all day on the Cutting Room Floor, while Mommy earns the Union Scale, for helping Jimmy cut it.

And working in the same Cutting Room for five years with Jimmy McCoy, has been a great deal more entertaining than the Films Mommy works on. For his wittysisms are never cut by any Board of Censures and, if he is in a particuler good mood (like when we are working on some Documenterry that doesn't have any actors in it) Jimmy sings all day long, with as good a voice as Mommy ever hears on sound tracks.

And working for a small salary, has given my Mouse Security, at last. Because, once our Govermint decides that some Film Star is never going to earn any more large salaries, it is forced to cancel our back Income Tax. For, being in the same Brackits with persons whose income is permanint, Uncle Sam has got to realize its only natural if we ultimitely go broke.

And, now that I've quit acting, it doesn't matter if the Film I'm working on is any good or not. For I will always have a profession which is based on a defanate knowledge of what I am doing (which few Film Stars ever adiquintly find out).

And there are other satisfactions, too, about cutting Film, because yesterday I thought up a way to deleet a big Close-Up of Inga Swansen out of her new picture.

Well, looking out the window, now little Mouse, I note its getting day-light, so Madge will be coming for you soon, and I'll be left alone, except for Jimmy at the Studio. But just now I'm beginning to remember that every time I ever asked any of those Husbands if they respeckted Mommy, their answer has inveritably been in the afirmitiff. But look what always happened! So I am beginning to wonder if maybe girls wouldn't be happier if we stopped demanding so much respeckt for ourselves and developped a little more respeckt for husbands.

And so, this morning, when Mommy walks into the Cutting Room, I may give Jimmy a surprize. Because he's always telling Mommy I have no gratitood and calling me an "Empty Sandwich." So, this morning, I'm going to recount to Jimmy all the wonderful things he's always doing for the Mouse and I. And then I'll tell him how deeply grateful we both are to Unity.

Well, I can see my Mouse begin to stir, so now I know you'll soon be hungry, and I'm going to just slip away to the kitchenette and cook us a delicious breakfast. And this morning we'll use the rest of the ice cream Andy brought in yesterday for your Birthday Party, and start to have our Pan Cakes Alla Mode. For Mommy might as well give up trying, any more, to slenderize,

213

because Jimmy McCoy is so masculine that he even admires hips.

And after breakfast, we'll have time for one last romp in the back yard while we're waiting for Madge (unless the weather suddenly gets bad). For, as our old friend, Joe Frisco, sometimes remarks,

"Nobody can tell about this California climate. One minit its hot and the next minit its cold, so a person never knows what to hock."

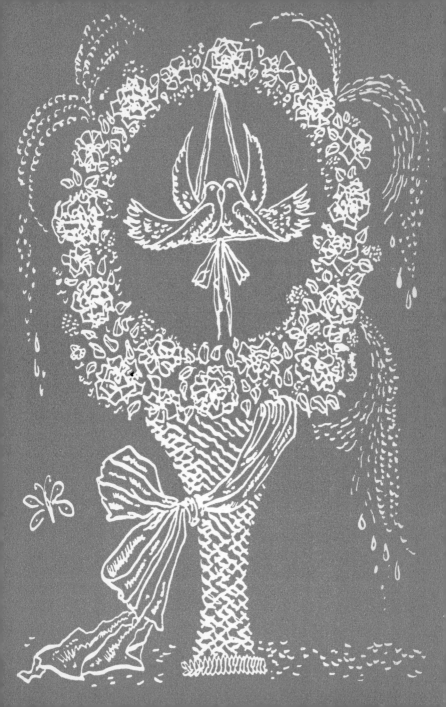